WELCOMING JESUS

Carol Clark Castro

Wm. C. Brown Company Publishers
Religious Education Division

Nihil Obstat:

Reverend Norman J. Belval
   Director of Religious Education,
   Archdiocese of Hartford

Imprimatur:

+ John F. Hackett, D.D.
   Auxiliary Bishop of Hartford
   Vicar General

October 24, 1978

Consultants

Reverend James A. O'Donohoe, J.C.D., St. John's Seminary, Brighton, Massachusetts

Sister Kathleen Hagerty, C.S.J., Assistant to the Director of Religious Education Programs for the Schools, Archdiocese of Boston, Boston, Massachusetts

Robert J. Fitzsimmons, Ph.D., Religious Education Coordinator, St. Paul's Church, Kensington, Connecticut

Credits

Cover Design: Craig M. Brown
Illustrations: Don Robison
Photographs: Bob Coyle—iv, 4, 5, 13, 16, 20, 21, 22, 30, 31, 34, 35, 44, 45, 46, 56, 63, 64, 66, 67, 68, 73, 85, 86, 87, 88, 92, 94, 95, 96, 98, 100, 101, 102, 103, 104, 105, 110, 111, 112
           Fr. Louis Cremonie—55
           Vivienne della Grotta—76, 77, 78, 79, 93
           Carol Deprez—32, 74
           John D. Firestone and Associates, Inc.—11, 14, 15, 24, 25
           Jim Shaffer—3, 62, 65, 67
           U.S. Department of Agriculture—60, 61

ISBN 0–697–01702–8

CONTENTS

Introduction

Dear Parents:

Your child is preparing for First Holy Communion. This is a time of eager anticipation for all concerned: soon he or she will join fully with you and the parish community in the celebration of the Eucharist.

During these weeks it will be your privilege to lead your child toward this new stage in his or her relationship with Jesus and the Church. It may be hoped that through sharing the stories, activities and prayer experiences found in these pages, not only your child, but the entire family will begin to discover new meaning in the Mass.

How to Use This Book

Each lesson begins with a *story* based on a situation from the child's everyday experience. While your child may never have experienced the exact circumstances described, it is hoped that he or she will be able to identify with the thoughts and feelings of the central character.

The stories speak of relationships in the child's life: give and take in the family, the effort to get along with peers, the experience of being touched by the needs of others and reaching out to help. The Mass is a celebration of God our Father's love for us. The purpose of the stories is to help your child recognize the active presence of God's love expressed in the loving words and actions of those who touch his or her life each day. It is to help your child see in these relationships an invitation to return this love by giving with generosity and receiving with gratitude.

You and your child should read each story together. Choose a quiet time when you have a few minutes to spend. Read it slowly. Stop whenever it may seem appropriate to relate what is happening to your own family life: Does this remind you of the time when . . . ? Have you ever felt that way? What do you think I would do in that situation? The story is meant to open for you insights into the thoughts and feelings of your child, to give you the opportunity to share your thoughts and feelings with him or her.

A *Bible story* is an integral part of each lesson. The Mass is a celebration of the Presence of Jesus among us, a thankful remembering of His self-giving love, fully expressed in His death and resurrection. Each story centers on Jesus, the One Who nourished the world with His Father's love by giving His life for us. These stories offer a vivid picture of Jesus involved in loving relationships with people. You can help your child to understand that it is this same Jesus Who lives today, Who loves and cares for him or her as He cared for the people of Palestine long ago. You can help your child anticipate Holy Communion as an invitation from Jesus to join with Him in loving the Father—and sharing the Father's love with others.

The *activities* included in each lesson are meant to be a family experience. The child is urged to seek help and advice in completing each project. Some activities invite the participation of *every* family member. All are meant to be shared with others.

Each lesson also includes a *prayer experience*. Most often these family celebrations are modelled on the Eucharist, including a sharing of God's Word through the reading of the Bible story and, frequently, a sharing of food as a sign of communion in the family.

These experiences, in addition to enriching your family life, will also help your child to recognize the parish Eucharist as a celebration of God's love, the means given by Jesus of growing in unity with God and with each other.

While such family prayer is an essential ingredient of this program, it is to be emphasized that these services are to be used with freedom and flexibility. Each family situation is unique. It is most important to pray together in a way that is comfortable and meaningful for you.

One key factor in your child's appreciation of the Eucharist will be his or her understanding of and familiarity with the ritual itself. The celebration will be truly his or her own thanksgiving to God only when he or she can participate completely and confidently in the community prayer and action. The final section of each lesson, *Getting Ready for Mass* is designed to help your child in this regard. These pages provide simple explanations of the Mass rituals and prayers.

You are encouraged to use the *Getting Ready for Mass* topics in a parent-child conversation on the day or evening before weekly Mass. At the Eucharist itself invite your child to be especially aware of these aspects of the celebration.

It is unquestionably true that your own sincere and wholehearted participation in the Eucharist celebration is the best guarantee that your child will discover the central role of the Eucharist in the life of a Catholic Christian. May these weeks of preparation be a source of new understanding and appreciation for you, your First-Communion child, and the entire family.

Getting Ready for Mass

Each week the members of God's family come together for a celebration. (A celebration means coming together with our friends to show how happy and thankful we feel about someone we love and the great things that person has done.)

At our celebration we remember the great gifts God has given us. We celebrate our thanks and joy.

> *We thank God our Father Who loves and cares for us.*
> *We thank Jesus Who died for us and rose to new life.*
> *We thank God the Holy Spirit Who lives in us and helps us.*

One name for this "thank-you" celebration is the **Mass.**
Its other name is **Eucharist. Eucharist** means "thanksgiving."
Can you think of one thing for which you would like to thank God at Mass this week? Write it here.

LESSON 1
Jesus Is with Us: Let's Celebrate

Jodie had been lonely. For many weeks she had not heard that special "good morning" knock on her bedroom door. When she went to wash up, she no longer found that smiling face drawn on the steamy bathroom mirror. And when she was late for the bus, no rumbly Jeep was waiting to give her a ride.

Jodie's brother had not seemed so very important when she saw him every day. But after he left for college, the family didn't seem to laugh so much at dinner time. She missed the guitar sounds coming from his room, and the thump of the basketball on the driveway. He had taught her how to shoot a basket. He would invite her to watch his team play ball in the park. And sometimes on the way home he would buy her ice cream.

Now she wondered, had he forgotten all about her while he was away? Had he missed her too? Any minute now he would be home and she would know the answer.

The first thing that she heard was the rumbling roar of his Jeep turning into the driveway. Then she heard her mother's voice calling, "Jodie, he's here!" She didn't stop to peek out the window, she went dashing straight down the stairs and out the front door.

He was running too. He picked her up and spun her around. "Boy, am I glad to see you!" he said.

Jodie was too out of breath to say anything at all, so she just smiled.

Have you ever missed someone?
How did you celebrate when that person came home again?
How do you suppose Jodie and her family celebrated when her brother came home?

DRAW A PICTURE OF THE CELEBRATION HERE.

Do you remember how Jesus died on the cross?
On that sad day His apostles thought they would never see Him again.

What a great surprise they had on Easter Sunday.
Jesus came to them. He was truly alive. He was wonderfully happy.
When He looked at them and spoke kind words to them, they felt peaceful and happy too.

For many days Jesus visited with His friends.
Then one day He asked them all to meet Him on a certain hilltop.
This would be the last time He would visit with them in this way.
He wanted to say good-bye.

Jesus did not want His friends to be unhappy.
He wanted them to know: "I am going to be with My Father.
You will no longer see My face or hear My voice.
But I will still be loving you, just as My Father loves you.
I will still be watching over you, just as He does.
I will be with you always."

Before Jesus left His followers He said, "Wait for the gift My Father promised . . . the gift I told you about."
Jesus had promised His friends that He and His Father would send them the gift of their Holy Spirit.

7

The Holy Spirit would keep them always close to God His Father, to Him, and to each other.

This promise made Jesus' friends hopeful and happy.
They said "good-bye" to Him and hurried home to the city of Jerusalem.
They stayed together like one big family with Mary, the mother of Jesus, and the apostles.
They prayed to God our Father.

The days went by: one, two, three. . . .

On the morning of the tenth day they heard a strange and wonderful sound, like a great wind blowing.
It filled the whole room.
They could feel its power moving around them.
When they looked up they saw something that looked like shining flames spreading out to touch each person.
The flames did not hurt or burn.
Instead, each person's heart was touched with joy.
What great love they began to feel for God our Father, for Jesus, for each other!

They could not see the Holy Spirit, but they knew He had come to stay

with them because of the wonderful changes happening in their hearts.
They knew Jesus was keeping His promise to be with them always.

They wanted to run out and share their happiness with the whole world.

They threw open the doors.
The street outside was crowded with people.

Peter the apostle called to them: "See how glad we are?
It is because God our Father has kept His promise.
Jesus and His Father have sent their Holy Spirit as a gift to us.
It is the Holy Spirit Who is making us so joyful.
He will stay with us always as Jesus promised.
Would you like to receive the Holy Spirit?" Peter asked.
"Yes!" many of the people answered. "What must we do?"
"Be sorry for the selfish things you have done.
Believe that Jesus is God's own Son Who loves you very much.
Be baptized and join our family, the family of those who believe in Jesus."

What a celebration the followers of Jesus must have had that day!
They thanked God our Father and Jesus for sharing their Holy Spirit with them.
Now they could be close to Jesus and each other always.

A FAMILY PRAYER CELEBRATION

(Note: After parent and child have shared the stories and activities for this lesson, include other family members in the planning of this celebration.)

Preparing for the Celebration

Explain the purpose of the celebration in words similar to the following:

Jesus is with us now. His Spirit lives in us.

Would you like to thank Jesus and His Father for sending their Spirit to us?

Would you like to prepare a celebration to give thanks to Jesus Who is with us always?

Here are some things which your family might like to do in honor of Jesus. Look over the list together. Choose the activities which your family likes best, or create activities of your own. Divide the work among family members. Let each person do the activity he or she prefers:

1. Find a favorite picture or statue of Jesus (or create one of your own). Put it in a place of honor in the room where your celebration will be held.
2. Prepare decorations to place near the picture of Jesus. Candles and flowers may be used.
3. Plan a parade in Jesus' honor. Make banners or signs to carry in the parade.
4. Prepare a cake or other special dessert to share.
5. Sing a song to praise and thank Jesus. Perhaps someone knows a song which he or she can teach the entire family.
6. Make up a prayer of thanks or a poem to Jesus.
7. Read aloud the story of Jesus sending the Holy Spirit which is found on pp. 7-9 of this lesson.

Turn to p. 113 in this book. You will find something to make for your celebration. Perhaps the child who is preparing for First Communion would enjoy this activity.

Read over the sample celebration which follows. <u>Adapt it to your family style.</u> Assign roles. Become familiar with prayer responses.

A SAMPLE CELEBRATION

(Note: This celebration may appropriately be used as a "grace" before meals. This outline is offered only as a guide. *Each family is encouraged to create a celebration according to their unique style.)*

Recalling the Presence of Jesus

The family may gather in a room other than the one in which the table has been prepared.

Leader: *It is good to be with people we love.*
They make us feel welcome and safe.
Let us remember Jesus Who loves us very much and is with us always.

Reader or Readers: (The story of Jesus sending the Holy Spirit, which is found on pp. 7-9 of this lesson, may be read aloud. If preferred, family members may share prayers or poems which they have prepared in Jesus' honor.)

The family may parade to the room where they will gather around the table. Banners and signs may be carried. Music may be played or a song may be sung.

Welcoming Jesus through Renewal of Baptismal Promises

Parent: (When all are standing near their places at table) *When each of you was newly born we brought you to the church to be baptized. We wanted you to receive the gift of the Holy Spirit from Jesus and His Father.*
We wanted you to be part of Jesus' Catholic family.
We cannot see the Holy Spirit, but we believe He lives in us.
He keeps us close to Jesus and each other.
Let us pretend that we are the people in the story we have just heard, and that Peter is speaking to us.

Getting Ready for Mass

As we enter the church building we notice near the door a small bowl filled with water. This special water is called **holy water.** The bowl is called the **holy water font.** People dip the fingers of their right hand into this holy water. Then they make the Sign of the Cross.

In the name of the Father and of the Son, and of the Holy Spirit. Amen.

The holy water reminds us of the water which was poured on our foreheads the day we were baptized.

Reader (taking the role of Peter): *Are you sorry for the selfish things which you have done against God and one another?*

All: *We are.*

Reader: *Do you believe that Jesus is God's Son and our King? Do you believe that He is with us always?*

All: *We do.*

Reader: *Do you want the Holy Spirit as your Friend and Helper? Will you welcome Him in your hearts?*

All: *We will.*

Parent and all: *In the name of the Father, and of the Son, and of the Holy Spirit. Amen.*

Parent: *The Lord be with you.*

All: *And also with you.*

(Members of the family may smile, clap, embrace or shake hands. The meal may begin.)

13

LESSON 2
Jesus Fills Us with Good Things

Chris was feeling very unhappy as he stepped from the school bus. All the way up the street he planned what to say to his mother. He had to let her know how much he hurt inside. But he was ashamed to tell her the terrible things those kids had said. Maybe he would wait 'til later.

"Is that you, Chris?" his mother called when she heard the door bang.

"Yep." He went into the kitchen where she was working at the table. "What are you making?" he asked.

"Bread," she answered.

"Good. I'm hungry."

"Why not have an apple?"

Chris looked inside the refrigerator. Then he shut the door. "I guess I'm not hungry after all." He stood watching his mother work. It was very quiet. "Do you think I'm smart?" he asked.

"Why, I know you are," she said. Then she looked at Chris's face. "Is something wrong?" she asked. "Do you want to tell me?"

Oh yes, he did! But he could feel the tears starting, so he talked as quickly as he could. "The kids laughed at me! They called me stupid."

His mother put down her rolling pin and reached for his hand.

"I didn't know the answer," he said. "I made mistakes in front of everyone. I *am* stupid!"

His mother squeezed his hand and went to put the bread pans in the oven. "Do you have your book?" she asked.

He nodded his head, "yes."

"You find the problem. I'll get a glass of milk for you and a cup of tea for me. Here where it is quiet the two of us will find the answer."

They sat side by side. His mother asked questions. Chris helped her to understand. They came to the part where he had been so mixed up. She sipped her tea as he thought about it.

Suddenly he could remember the sound of the teacher's voice explaining what to do. He had just been too frightened to understand. Now it seemed easy.

"See, mom," he said wiggling excitedly in his chair, "this is how you get the answer!"

"Well, well," she said, "I knew you were smart." And she winked at him.

The friendly smell of the bread was beginning to warm the whole room. "Guess what," Chris smiled. "My hungry feeling is growing again."

What did Chris need when he came home from school?
How did his mother help him?
How does your family help you when you need

—someone to listen to your news?
—someone to answer a question?
—someone to cheer you up when you are unhappy?
—someone to feed you when you are hungry?

Can you remember a time when someone in your family helped you in one of these ways? Tell about it.

Here are some other ways in which people in your family may help you:

—caring for you when you are sick
—taking you where you need to go
—buying what you need
—correcting you when you are doing wrong
—playing a game with you
—saying "I love you"
—laughing at your joke
—telling you that you have done a good job

Think of the people in your family. Remember one thing each of them has done to help you. Perhaps someone will help you to remember. Then turn to p. 115 in this book. **There you will find something you may do to say "thank you" to each one.**

A Story from Mark 6:30-44

Everyone in the whole town wanted to be with Jesus.
Why, He and His friends had so much company, there was not even time to eat and talk together.
So Jesus said to them, "Let us go off by ourselves to some place where we will be alone and you can rest a while."

Jesus and His happy apostles quickly left the house, hurried to the lake shore nearby, and climbed into Peter's fishing boat.

Just as they were setting out across the lake, some people came running down to the beach.
They shaded their eyes to get a better look.
Was that Jesus in the boat? Yes, it was!
They wanted so much to see Him.
Maybe they could run along the shore and meet Jesus when He reached the other side.
So they started off. Others joined them along the way.
One person told another. Soon many people were hurrying to meet Jesus.

When Jesus and His friends climbed from the boat, what a surprise was waiting!
Their grassy picnic spot far from every town was crowded with people.
How disappointed the apostles must have felt.
Perhaps they wanted to climb right back in the boat.

But Jesus could not leave. He felt sorry for these people.
How hot and tired they looked!
They must need His help very much to have run so far.

So Jesus answered their questions.

He made sick people well.
He cheered those who were worried or sad.
He spoke to them about God our Father, Who loves and cares for every one of His children.

The day passed quickly.
The apostles were getting very hungry.
They could hear children beginning to cry for their suppers.

So they went to Jesus and whispered, "It is already very late, and this is a lonely place. Send the people away, and let them go to the nearby farms and villages and buy themselves something to eat."

Jesus knew this would be hard for the people to do.
There were so many of them!
Perhaps some of them had no money.

So He said to His friends, "How much bread do you have?
Go and see."

After a while the apostles came back and told Jesus, "We have only five loaves of bread and two fish."
What a small amount of food for such a large crowd!

Jesus said, "Tell the people to sit down in groups."
He looked at the crowds scattered over the hillside.
In their brightly colored clothes they looked like giant flowerbeds blooming everywhere.

Jesus took the bread and fish in His hands and said a prayer of thanks to His Father.
Then He broke the bread and fish in pieces.
He handed some to each of His apostles and said, "Share these with the people."

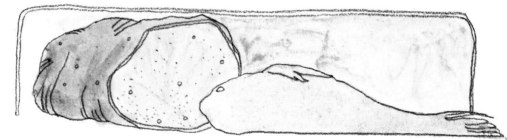

The apostles did not understand.
What would happen when this little bit of food ran out and they still had many, many hungry people to feed?
But they trusted Jesus.
They knew God the Father would hear His prayer.
He would not let His children go hungry.

As the apostles handed out the food, something wonderful happened.
No matter how much bread and fish they gave away, there was still enough for the next person.
Soon every one was filled, and there were twelve baskets of food left over!

Jesus must have smiled.
He had spent the day giving God's hungry children what they needed. He had given them Himself.

Thinking About the Story

Jesus knows what each person needs. He knows when a person is hungry for food, or for answers to questions, or for love. Jesus wants to feed us. He is happy when we go to Him so that He can share Himself with us. He wants us to ask His help for ourselves and for others.

Is there something you would like to ask of Jesus now? Write it here.

A FAMILY SHARING CELEBRATION

(Note: After parent and child have shared the stories and activities for this lesson, include other family members in the planning of this celebration.)

Preparing the Celebration

Explain the purpose of the celebration in words similar to the following:

> *When the members of our family sit down together to share a good meal which everyone has helped to prepare, it is a fine way of remembering all the times we help each other and share with one another every day.*

Here are some chores which are part of preparing for every meal. Ask each member of the family to choose the job which he or she is willing to do as part of this sharing celebration:

1. Be sure the room in which the family will eat is neat and clean.
2. Set the table.
3. Prepare decorations for the table.
4. Prepare the food (the chief cook may divide these chores among those willing to help).
5. Serve the meal.
6. Clear the table.
7. Wash dishes.
8. Be sure the room is neat and clean following the meal.

If someone knows how to bake bread, perhaps he or she would be willing to make a loaf especially for this celebration. Perhaps the child preparing for First Communion would be allowed to help.

Explain the "thank you" note project on p. 115 of this book. Invite all to participate.

Read over the sample celebration which follows. Adapt it to your family style. Assign roles. Become familiar with the prayer responses.

A SAMPLE CELEBRATION

(Note: This celebration may be held at the dining table as the meal is about to begin.)

Remembering Jesus Who Cares for Our Needs

Reader: (The story of Jesus feeding the people found on pp. 17-19 of this lesson may be read aloud.)

Leader: *Let us think quietly for a few moments of something we want or need for ourselves, our family, or others. Perhaps each would like to say a silent prayer asking Jesus to help us, to share Himself with us. Anyone who wishes may share his or her prayer with all of us by saying it aloud.* (Allow sufficient time for individuals to respond.)

Sharing Thank You Notes

Leader: *One way in which Jesus helps us is through one another. Every day the Spirit of Jesus living in us helps us to care about each other and to share what we have. Let us say "thank you" to one another now by presenting the "thank you" notes we have prepared.* (All may exchange and read notes.)

Sharing the Bread

Parent: (with the loaf of bread before him or her)

Thank You, Father, for feeding Your hungry children. Thank You for sending Your Spirit to help us love one another. Just as Jesus, Your Son, shared bread with Your hungry people, we want to share this food as a sign of our love for You and for each other.

All: *In the name of the Father, and of the Son, and of the Holy Spirit. Amen.*

(The bread may be passed. Each person may take a piece, not for himself or herself, but to exchange with the person next to him or her. When all have received some bread, each person may exchange his or her piece with someone else using the greeting:

The Lord be with you.

And also with you.

The meal may follow.)

In the place of honor in the church we see the **altar.**
The altar is a table.

On this altar we place bread and wine. During Mass this food becomes the sign of the thank-you gift we are offering to God. Jesus invites us to share this special food from God's table.

Near the altar is a **cross.**
The cross helps us to remember how Jesus died for us.
It tells how much Jesus loves us.
It tells how much Jesus loves God our Father.

Would you like to draw a picture of the altar and cross in your church in the space below?

LESSON 3
Jesus Helps Us to Forgive One Another

The Racers' midget hockey team had lost three games in a row. The coach called a meeting. "Boys and girls," he began, "each one of you skates well. Each one knows how to play the game. Why do you think we have not been playing well?"

"It's all Greg's fault," Joe called out. "He's always breaking the rules."

"You should talk," Greg answered back. "You act like you're the only one who can make a goal."

"I never get a chance to make a goal," Janet said.

"That's 'cause you're a fraidy cat," Joe told her.

"That's right, Jan," Bobby agreed. "If you would only push your way through like I've told you . . ."

Barbara spoke up for Jan, "Oh, Bobby, you're just too bossy!"

"So what? You never listen anyway!"

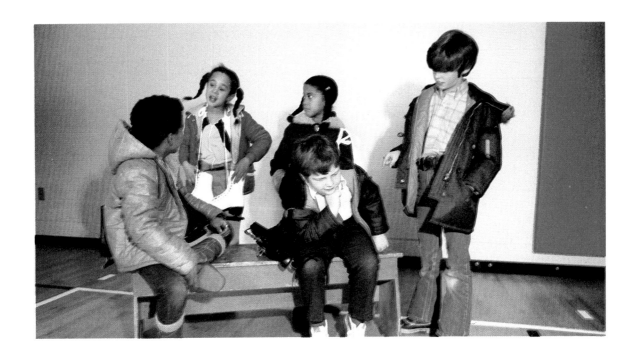

"That's enough!" the coach said in a strong voice. "Quiet down and think about what you are doing to one another. Then you may see why no one is doing his or her best."

Everyone became very still. The coach stood and watched them. Some looked angry. Some looked a little frightened. Janet had begun to cry.

"We all feel bad because we are losing," the coach said. "It is easy to blame others. That only makes every one feel worse. What can we do?"

After a while Barbara spoke in a small voice. "Maybe we could try saying nice things."

It became very quiet again. The members of the team sat looking at one another.

"Bobby is smart," Barbara began shyly.

"Barbara never misses practice," Bobby said, smiling.

"Greg skates fast," Joe shouted.

"And Joe never gives up," Greg called back.

"Jan watches every move of the game. She always knows where her help is needed most," the coach said, squeezing her shoulder.

"And in our next game you are going to make a goal," Greg told her. "We will help you."

"Hey, we may even win!" Janet laughed.

And everyone cheered.

Can you see some reasons why the Racers were not playing well?
Do you think they will play better during their next game? Why?
The boys and girls had treated each other selfishly at times. They said
unkind things to one another. Do you think they were sorry? How did they
show it?
Did you ever belong to a team in your neighborhood? In school? In sports?

A Story from Luke 15:1-7

Many kinds of people came to Jesus.
Sometimes the rich people with fine clothes would frown at those who
were poor.

Those who could stand tall and run fast often looked the other way when
someone who was sick passed by.
The people who thought they were very smart would shake their fingers at
those who were too young to keep still.
And the people who thought they were very good would look at those
who had done wrong and whisper to one another, "Why is Jesus welcoming such bad people?
Why He even eats with them!"

Jesus would look at all these people. He loved every one.
They were all His brothers and sisters, children of God our Father.

He wanted them to welcome and forgive one another.
So He told them a story.

"Once there was a shepherd," Jesus began.
"This shepherd had one hundred sheep to care for.
It kept him very busy.

Each night the shepherd gathered his sheep in a safe yard with a high
stone wall around it.
He would sleep near the gate so that no wolves or thieves could sneak in
to harm them.

Early each morning he led his sheep to a grassy place with a pool of cool
water.
Here they could eat and drink while the shepherd watched over them.

In the evening he would count them as they went through the gate into the
yard.
He wanted to be sure every one was safe.

One night he counted all the way to ninety-nine.
Then he looked around.
Where was number one hundred?
He counted again just to be sure. It was true.
One of the lambs was lost!

It was almost dark.
The shepherd knew his lamb would feel frightened.
Perhaps a wolf might try to eat him up!

Quickly the shepherd locked the gate so that no one could harm the other sheep or take them away.
Then he grabbed his big stick and hurried off.

At last, far from home, he heard the shaky cry of the little lamb.
He felt his way in the dark, following the sound.
Then he saw it—a small patch of white, shivering in the shadows.

The shepherd grinned with happiness as he lifted the lamb to his shoulders.
When at last he could see the light shining in the window of his own house, he began taking giant steps and shouting to his wife and children, Let's celebrate!
I found him—I found my lamb!

Everyone came running out to hug the lamb and laugh for joy.
The ninety-nine sheep were happy too."

Jesus is like the good shepherd. He loves and cares for all of us. He wants us to love and care for one another. Sometimes each one of us can act like the lost lamb. We are so busy doing what we please that we forget how others feel, or how busy they are, or how much worry we may be causing them. When we act in this way we make others unhappy. We make ourselves unhappy. Jesus wants us to know that when this happens, He still loves us. He is ready to forgive us so that we may be part of one happy family again.

Here are some ways that people in families may stray away from one another:

- going to play right after a meal and leaving the clean-up for others
- using things, then forgetting to put them away so that others have to look and look for what they need
- making noise when someone needs quiet to think or listen
- taking the best so that others have only leftovers

Can you think of some other way in which a person might act selfishly at home? **Write it here**.

Think quietly: Have I done any of these selfish things?
   How can I show Jesus I am truly sorry?
   What can I do to make up to others?

A FAMILY SERVICE OF FORGIVENESS

(Note: After parent and child have shared the stories and activities for this lesson, include other family members in the planning of this celebration.)

Preparing for the Celebration

Before the service a paper lamb should be made for each member of the family, using the pattern on p. 17. The child preparing for First Communion may enjoy doing this.

Read over the sample celebration which follows. Adapt it to your family style. Assign roles. Become familiar with prayer responses (especially note the spontaneous prayers suggested in the sections titled "Asking Forgiveness of Jesus and One Another" and "Asking the Help of Jesus, the Good Shepherd." Family members may wish to give some thought to these before the service.)

A SAMPLE CELEBRATION

(Note: This service may be held at any time convenient for the family, e.g., in the evening after supper. The paper lambs should be placed in the center of the family group.)

Asking Forgiveness of Jesus and One Another

Reader: (The story of the good shepherd, which is found on pp. 26-28 of this lesson, may be read aloud.)

Leader: *When we act selfishly, we are something like the lost sheep in the story. We stray from Jesus. We stray from each other. Let us each try to remember one way in which we may have acted selfishly toward one another.*

When you have thought of something, take your lamb. Perhaps as you do this, you would like to ask forgiveness of the family, at least by saying, "I am sorry."

(It would be helpful if one of the parents went first to show the way. A formula similar to the following might be used:

I am sorry for tying up the telephone so long. Please forgive me.

or

I am sorry for pouting at the dinner table the other night. Please forgive me.)

Hiding the Lambs

When everyone in the family has claimed his or her lamb, the announcement may be made: *Now let us hide our lambs.* The group may scatter, each hiding his or her lamb within a designated area.

Seeking the Lost Lambs

When all have returned to the group after hiding their lambs the leader may offer ideas similar to the following: *If we have strayed like the lost lamb, how can we find our way home again? We need someone who cares enough to come looking for us. We need someone to tell us, "I forgive you." Someone has to help us do better. As a sign of our love and care for one another, let us go now to look for one another's lambs and bring them back to their owners.*

Each family member should find one lamb other than his or her own. When all have returned to the group, each person may give the lamb he or she has found to its owner. Some sign of forgiveness, natural to those involved, may be used: a smile, a hug, a handshake.

31

A prayer similar to the following may be used to close the service. Specific examples more closely related to family experiences should be used if these do not apply.

Leader: *Jesus, sometimes we miss the chance to help someone who has a lot of work to do. Lord, have mercy.*

All: *Lord, have mercy.*

Leader: *Jesus, sometimes we miss the chance to be with someone who needs us to listen to a story or play a game. Christ, have mercy.*

All: *Christ, have mercy.*

Leader: *Jesus, sometimes we think only of what we want instead of giving others a chance to do things their way. Lord, have mercy.*

All: *Lord, have mercy.*

Leader: *Let us say the* **Lord's Prayer** *together as a sign of our belonging to God the Father, to Jesus and to each other. Let us pay special attention to the words "forgive us our trespasses as we forgive those who trespass against us." This means, "God, please forgive me for the selfish things I have done to others. In just the same way I will forgive anyone who has hurt me."*

All: *Our Father. . . .*

(A family activity, such as a game or excursion in which all participate would form a fitting conclusion to this service. When we have sincerely forgiven one another, we are ready to celebrate as one family.)

People wear clothes which match the things they do.
Our priest wears special clothes at Mass, because Mass is special.
We call the priest's clothes **vestments.**

A. The first vestment the priest puts on is a long, white gown called an **alb.**

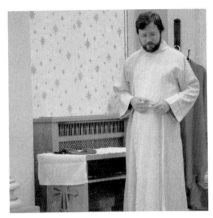

B. Next the priest ties a cord around his waist.

C. Then the priest puts a long piece of cloth around his neck. It is called a **stole.**

D. Over all these vestments, the priest wears a large, colorful robe called a **chasuble.**

The color of the chasuble may be purple, white, red, or green. Our priest wears purple during the four weeks before Christmas and the six weeks before Easter.
He wears white during the happy times of Christmas and Easter. To celebrate the happy days of Pentecost the priest wears red. In summer and fall the priest wears green, the color of growing plants, since this is the time we continue to grow.

What color chasuble is our priest wearing now?

LESSON 4
Jesus Nourishes Us with His Word

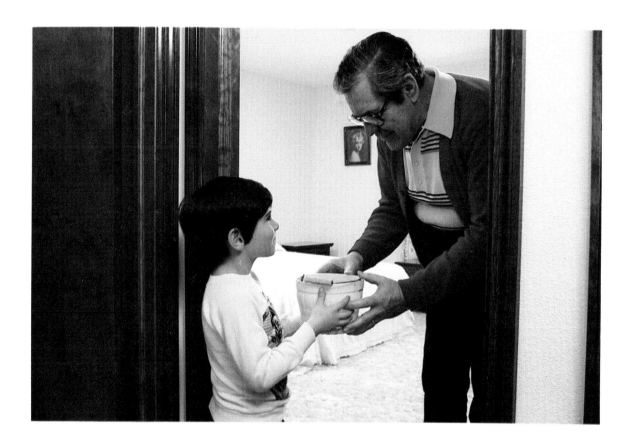

Eddie liked to visit his grandfather's room. When he had some good news to tell or a question to ask, he would knock on grandpa's door. Then a glad voice would call, "Is that you, Ed? Come on in!"

No matter what Eddie needed to know, his grandfather would always begin his answer in the same way: "That reminds me of a story . . ." Grandpa told exciting stories about flying an airplane, working for a circus and living on a farm.

He had stories which helped Eddie to understand unpleasant things like why he couldn't eat cookies before supper and why he had to go to bed early. They were funny stories which laughed Eddie's grouchy feelings away.

One day Eddie ran to his grandfather and said, "Look at the turtle I found!" That made grandpa remember the time he and Eddie's dad had found a turtle with yellow spots on its black shell. "Oh," Eddie said. "Did dad keep him as a pet?" "No," grandpa answered, "Your dad was afraid he might get lonesome for the other turtles." "I never thought of that," Eddie said. "Do you suppose we could visit this turtle down at the pond?" "Good idea!" grandpa said, "Let's take him home now."

Once grandpa told Eddie the story of a windy spring day when he and Eddie's dad first flew a kite together. "That sounds like fun!" Eddie grinned. Grandpa walked out on the porch, breathed deep and said, "I feel just like flying a kite today. Want to come along?"

On rainy days Eddie would take out the old album filled with pictures of his dad when he was a young boy. Eddie would let the book flop open on grandpa's lap, close his eyes and point to one of the pictures. "Tell me the story of this one," he would beg. Then grandpa would tell the story of the picnic, the sled ride, the school play.

"Dad was a lot like me, wasn't he grandpa?" Eddie asked.

"Yes, he was," grandpa agreed.

"Do you think I'll be like him someday?"

"I wouldn't be surprised," grandpa smiled.

"Good," Eddie said. "It will be fun telling stories to someone like me."

Why did Eddie like his grandfather's stories?

Can you name some things he learned from his grandfather?

Do you have someone who tells you stories? Who is it? What kind of stories does he or she tell? Do these stories
—tell of things that happened long ago?
—teach you how to do new things?
—give you wishes for the future?

Do your mom and dad have pictures of things they did when they were your age? Ask them to tell you the story of one of those pictures.

Do you have a picture of something you have done? Paste it on this page. Write the story of the picture on the same page. (You may write the story, even if you have no picture.) Perhaps someone will help you.

A Story from Luke 10:38-42

When Jesus walked from town to town, He would often stop at the homes of His friends.
Two of Jesus' best friends were Martha and Mary.
They were sisters, and both of them were very pleased whenever they saw Jesus at their door.

One day they invited Jesus in and gave Him a chair.
They had some fresh water to wash His hot, dusty feet.
Perhaps they gave Him a cool cup of wine to drink.

As Jesus rested, He began to talk.

He told His friends stories of the wonderful ways God our Father had helped His people long ago. He told how God was still showing His love for His children every day. He spoke of the places He had visited and the people He had helped.

Mary always had questions to ask. There were so many things she wanted to know about God our Father and how she could please Him more.

But after a few minutes Martha started to fidget in her chair.

She was thinking, "Soon it will be supper time.
Jesus must be hungry. He is such a special guest.
What shall I serve? Do we have enough?"

So Martha stood up and tiptoed from the room.
She didn't even know what a good story she was missing, because her ears had stopped listening.

She started opening cupboard doors, and rattling dishes, and stirring the stew. How busy she was!

She wanted to hear Jesus say, "My, what a good cook you are!"

But all the while Jesus was saying words which would have given Martha even greater joy, and she was missing them all.

Instead she was thinking, "Dinner will never be ready if I have to do it all alone. I can't set the table and watch the stew at the same time. Mary should know better than to sit there doing nothing when I need her help so much. I'm going to call her."

So Martha went right up to Jesus and said, "Lord, don't you care that my sister has left me to do all the work by myself? Tell her to come and help me!"
She did not even notice that she was interrupting what Jesus was saying.

Jesus became quiet and looked up at Martha.
He liked her very much, so He just shook His head and said slowly, "Martha, Martha! You are worried and troubled over so many things, but just one is needed. Mary has chosen the right thing. I came to visit because I have good news to share. I want to be with you. I don't need a fancy meal. Any food will taste good when we are listening to one another."

What did Martha do then? Maybe she took off her apron and sat down next to Mary. What do you think?

Thinking About the Story

Martha and Mary were very lucky to have Jesus as a friend. He helped them to remember the stories which told of God's love for His children. His words answered their questions, helped them to do good, made them peaceful and happy when they felt worried or afraid.

Jesus is our friend too. He wants us to hear words and stories that will help us. This is why He sends persons who speak these words to us. God had given Eddie a grandfather to whom he could listen. Whom has He sent to You? Perhaps Jesus has sent you messages such as these through your parents, teachers and friends:

"I love you."
"I forgive you."
"Do this. . . . Don't do that."
"Please."
"Thank you."
"This is the way to do it."

The words of our family and friends tell us that God our Father is thinking of us and caring for us each day. The stories of Jesus in the Bible help us to remember that God has always loved and cared for His children—and He always will.

The part of the Bible called the Gospel tells the story of Jesus: the words He said, the things He did, the stories He told. The word *Gospel* means "good news." Jesus wants us to read His good news messages in the Bible. He wants His Gospel story to make us glad, just as it did Martha and Mary. **Some stories from the Gospel are in this book. Can you find them?**

These are some words from the Gospel which Jesus spoke long ago. He still speaks these words to you and me today. You may want to remember these messages of Jesus at special times.

When you want to know how to please Jesus—

"My commandment is this: love one another, just as I love you. . . . You are my friends, if you do what I command you" (John 15:12,14).

When someone has hurt your feelings—

"If you forgive others the wrongs they have done you, your Father in heaven will also forgive you" (Matthew 6:14).

When you are wondering how to make someone happy—

"Do for others just what you want them to do for you" (Matthew 7:12).

When you have done something wrong and are sorry—

"Your sins are forgiven you, my friend" (Luke 5:20).

When you need something very much or you want to help someone else—

"The Father will give you whatever you ask of Him in my name" (John 15:16).

When you are worried about something—

"Peace I leave with you; my own peace I give you. . . . Do not be worried and upset; do not be afraid" (John 14:27).

Do you have a favorite word of Jesus from the Gospel? Write it here.

Choose one of the words of Jesus to learn by heart.

A FAMILY CELEBRATION OF THE GOOD NEWS

(Note: After parent and child have shared the stories and activities for this lesson, include other family members in the planning of this celebration.)

Preparing for the Celebration

Sometime before the service is to be held, ask each member of the family to look over the quotations from the Gospel found on p. 40 of this book. Ask him or her to select the one which he or she feels is most applicable to the family or to a particular member of the family. (A quotation other than those included on these pages may, of course, be chosen.) The quotation should be written out neatly on a piece of paper and brought to the service. Older family members may prefer to read their quotations directly from the Bible. Some may even wish to memorize their quotations. Read over the sample celebration which follows. Adapt it to your family style. Assign roles. Become familiar with prayer responses.

A SAMPLE CELEBRATION

(Note: This celebration may appropriately be used as an evening prayer or as a grace before meals.)

Introductory Prayer

Leader: *Jesus, we have come together as a family to listen to Your Word. We want to remember the great things You did for us—and the loving words You spoke. We know You love and care for us now and always. We will listen to Your good news with open ears and open hearts. Please help us to understand and to welcome Your message. We ask this of You Who live and reign with God the Father in the unity of the Holy Spirit, one God, forever and ever.*

All: *Amen.*

Leader: *The Lord be with you.*

All: *And also with you.*

Proclamation of the Good News

Each person in turn may be invited to share his or her Gospel quotation. The following formula may be used by each one.

Reader: *A reading from the holy Gospel according to (Matthew, Mark, Luke or John).*

All: *Glory to you, Lord.* (The Sign of the Cross may be made on the forehead, the lips and the heart with the thumb of the right hand.)

Reader: (Reading or recitation of the quotation he or she has chosen.)

Leader: (Following the reading of the last quotation) *This is the Gospel of the Lord.*

All: *Praise to You, Lord Jesus Christ.*

Following the Service

The meaning of particular quotations and the reasons why they were chosen may be shared. Those quotations which are most appropriate might be posted on a family bulletin board or message center.

The most important of all the readings at Mass is the **Gospel.**
It tells the story of the words and deeds of Jesus.
Only our priest (or a deacon) may read the Gospel message. The priest speaks for Jesus and the Gospel is Jesus' own message to us.

Our priest begins the reading with the words:
    A reading from the Gospel according to (Matthew, Mark, Luke, or John).
We answer:
    Glory to you, Lord.
(As these words are said a small Sign of the Cross may be made on our forehead, lips, and heart with the thumb of the right hand.)

When the Gospel reading is finished, the priest says:
    This is the Gospel of the Lord.
We answer:
    Praise to you, Lord Jesus Christ.

Ask someone in your family to show you how to make the small Sign of the Cross on your forehead, lips, and heart.

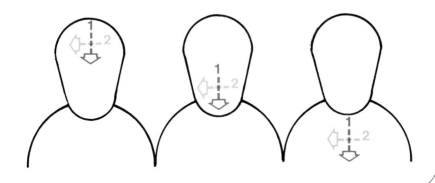

LESSON 5
Jesus Is with Us to Answer Our Needs

Patty and her older sister, Carol, delivered newspapers. Carol liked to check in her book the names of those who had paid. Patty liked to roll the papers and throw them on the porches. Both of them liked counting the money when they reached home.

Their parents put most of the money they earned in the bank. They said that some day it would help to pay for important things like going to college. But they did give each girl an allowance which she could spend for treats like the ice cream truck or the movies on Saturday afternoon.

Once in a while instead of spending their money for a candy bar or a balloon Patty and Carol would drop it in the mystery jar which they had hidden at the back of the bookshelf in their bedroom. On rainy days they

would shake the jar and spill the coins all over Carol's bed. Then they would sit and count them over and over.

Part of the game was planning how to spend the hidden treasure. "Maybe we could buy the matching dolls we didn't get for Christmas," Patty would say. "Or that electric game we saw advertised on T.V.," Carol would suggest. Then one day she said, "Maybe dad would even let us have a dog if he knew we had saved the money for it." Now that was the best idea of all!

But one afternoon something happened to change their plan. When they knocked on Mrs. Carey's door, she didn't come right away. "I can see her sitting in the kitchen," Patty said, looking through the window on the porch.

"Maybe the bell is broken," Carol guessed. She knocked twice and called, "Mrs. Carey, it's your papergirls."

They saw Mrs. Carey get up from her chair and walk toward them. When she opened the door she said, "I'm sorry, girls, I must have been dreaming. I didn't even hear the bell."

"That's all right," Carol told her.

While she was getting her purse, Patty whispered, "I think she's been crying."

"Me too," Carol whispered back.

As Mrs. Carey counted the money into Carol's hand, Patty asked, "Are you feeling all right today?"

"Do you need anything at the store?" Carol added.

Mrs. Carey tried to smile. "I'm fine, girls," she said. "It's just that sometimes I begin feeling very lonesome for my dog, Major, who died."

"Our supper isn't until five o'clock," Carol said. "May we visit for a little while?"

Mrs. Carey brought them each an apple. She showed them the flowers she was growing and the sweater she was knitting for her little granddaughter who lived far away. "Thank you, girls," she said as they were leaving. "Come again soon."

As they walked home Carol said, "Poor Mrs. Carey has to eat her supper all alone."

"And watch T.V. alone too," Patty added. "I wonder if she is scared at night."

"We're lucky," Carol said slowly. "We have one another and mom and dad."

"Soon we'll even have our dog!" Patty reminded her.

For a little while they just kept walking without saying a word.

"When we get home," Patty said at last, "let's count our money . . ."

"To see if we have enough to buy a dog," Carol chimed in.

"For Mrs. Carey!" Patty finished excitedly.

They both started running as fast as they could.

"Hey," Patty said as she climbed up to get the jar. "We're going to have to start our game all over again."

"Of course," Carol told her. "We may meet someone else who needs our help."

Whose help will Patty and Carol need in carrying out their plan?

Do you know someone who needs your help? **Place a star next to each item listed below if you know someone who has that kind of need.**

Someone who is sick

Someone who has trouble doing school work

Someone who is tired and has a lot of work to do

Someone who is feeling sad

Someone who is lonely

Someone who may need food or clothes

Someone who must stay home all the time

Can you think of one way in which you could help someone? **Write it here.**

Jesus and His friends were invited to a wedding.
Mary, the mother of Jesus, was invited too.
All the relatives, friends and neighbors came from far and near.
They sang and danced and laughed and talked.
And, of course, they had good things to eat and drink.

Now this wedding party lasted not just one day, but a whole week.
Think of all the bread and fish, all the meat, vegetables and wine that
would be needed to feed so many people for such a long time!

Dancing and talking can make you very hungry.
On the first two days there was plenty of food for everyone.
On the next two days there was enough.
But by the end of the week the waiters could see that the wine was not go-
ing to last.

Mary, the mother of Jesus, noticed the problem too.
"How embarrassing it will be for the family if they have no more wine to
share!" she thought.
It would spoil this happy party for the bride and groom.

Then Mary smiled to herself.
She knew this didn't have to happen.
She knew someone who could help. It was her son, Jesus.

Mary went to the spot where Jesus was laughing and talking with the other
guests.
She put her hand on His shoulder and whispered in His ear, "They are out
of wine."

Jesus listened. He did not say, "Yes, I will help."
He did not exactly say "no."

Mary knew Jesus cared for these people as much as she did.
She was certain that He would want to help.
So she went to the waiters and said to them,
"Do whatever He tells you."

Soon Jesus walked over to these waiters.
He looked at the six very large jars made of stone which had been filled
with water for the people to wash themselves. Now they were almost
empty.
"Fill these jars with water," He told the waiters.

When all the jars, filled to the very top, were standing in front of Jesus, He said, "Now draw some water out and take it to the man in charge of the feast."

The waiters must have looked at one another.
Water was only for washing. Wine was for drinking.
If they asked the head waiter to taste the water, he would think they were crazy. He might even fire them!

But Jesus seemed so sure it would be all right, that they did as He asked.

When the man in charge drank from the cup, he did not frown.
In fact, he looked happy and surprised.
He went running to the bridegroom and said, "You have kept the best wine until now!"

The bridegroom probably just nodded and said, "Thank you."
He did not really understand what had happened.
But the waiters knew.

And Mary and Jesus must have smiled at one another.

Jesus and Mary cared about their friends. They noticed right away when something was wrong. They were willing to do all they could to help. Jesus and Mary care for each one of us. They want to help us when we are in need.

Do you know this prayer to Mary, the mother of Jesus? It is a good way of asking her to pray to Jesus for us. Perhaps you would like to learn it. Ask someone in your family to help you.

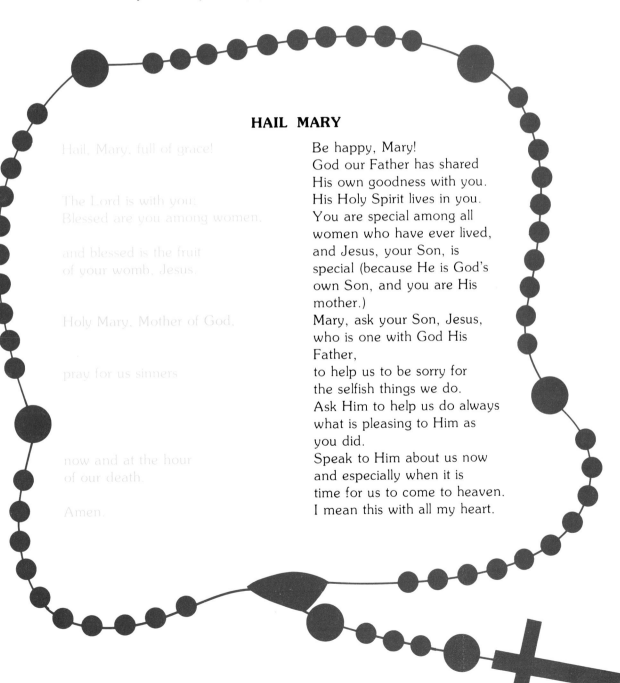

HAIL MARY

Hail, Mary, full of grace!

The Lord is with you;
Blessed are you among women,

and blessed is the fruit
of your womb, Jesus.

Holy Mary, Mother of God,

pray for us sinners

now and at the hour
of our death.

Amen.

Be happy, Mary!
God our Father has shared
His own goodness with you.
His Holy Spirit lives in you.
You are special among all
women who have ever lived,
and Jesus, your Son, is
special (because He is God's
own Son, and you are His
mother.)
Mary, ask your Son, Jesus,
who is one with God His
Father,
to help us to be sorry for
the selfish things we do.
Ask Him to help us do always
what is pleasing to Him as
you did.
Speak to Him about us now
and especially when it is
time for us to come to heaven.
I mean this with all my heart.

A FAMILY PRAYER CELEBRATION

(Note: After parent and child have shared the stories and activities for this lesson, include other family members in the planning of this celebration.)

Preparing for the Celebration

Explain the purpose of the celebration in words similar to the following:

> *In this time of family prayer we are going to bring our own needs and the needs of others to Jesus and His mother Mary. We are going to pray to them with confidence, knowing they will surely help us.*
> *We are aware, however, that the chief way in which Jesus answers our needs is through one another. His Spirit living in us helps us to notice these needs and gives us the love and courage necessary to help in any way we can. As part of our service we are going to ask Jesus and His mother to help us choose at least one way in which we as a family may reach out and help someone who needs us.*

Read over the sample celebration which follows. Adapt it to your family style. Assign roles. Become familiar with the prayer responses.

A SAMPLE CELEBRATION

(Note: This time of family conversation and prayer may be held whenever family members are available to spend a relaxed time together.)

Reflecting on Jesus' Concern for Others

Reader: (The story of the wedding feast at Cana, found on pp. 48-50 of this lesson may be read aloud.)

Leader: *Jesus always wants to answer our needs, just as He answered the needs of the people at the wedding feast. One way in which Jesus helps us is through each other. The Spirit of Jesus living in us helps us to see the needs of others. He gives us the desire to do something for these people. He shows us the best way to help.*

Think quietly for a moment of a time when someone helped you. Perhaps you were hunting for something you had lost. You may have been hurrying to finish some work or looking for someone to play a game with you. Someone noticed and came to help. Can you remember such a time?

Now remember a time when you have been this kind of friend to someone else. Maybe you felt like watching T.V. or going out with your friends. Instead you helped someone who needed you. It made that person glad, didn't it? How did it make you feel?

Family members may be invited to share memories of times when someone helped them, or they helped someone else. All should be encouraged to participate.

Leader: *In the story of the wedding feast it was Mary who asked Jesus to help her friends. We can be like Mary.*

Let us think of the persons we know: relatives, friends, neighbors, those with whom we share our hours at work or at school. What kinds of help do these people need? (Allow time for reflection.)

Perhaps we have learned of some peoples' needs through T.V. or the newspaper. Can you recall some of these?

Let us go to Jesus as a family and ask His help for each of these people.

Each person may offer one or more intentions. The following samples are offered only as a model—the family should make up prayers about the real needs in their own lives and the lives of others.

Speaker: *For our friend, _____ , who is sick, that she may feel better. We pray to the Lord.*

All: *Lord, hear our prayer.*

Speaker: *For _____ , who is out of work, that he may find a job. Let us pray to the Lord.*

All: *Lord, hear our prayer.*

Speaker: *For the people in the country of _____ , who do not have enough to eat, that food may be shared with them. We pray to the Lord.*

All: *Lord, hear our prayer.*

Speaker: *For a person with whom I work who has a drinking problem that he may be helped to overcome it. Let us pray to the Lord.*

All: *Lord, hear our prayer.*

Leader: *Let us pray the **Hail Mary** together, asking the mother of Jesus to remember all her children and join with us in asking the help of Jesus.*

All: *Hail Mary. . . .*

Planning a Family Project

Leader: *Think of the persons for whom we have just prayed. What could our family do to be of help to them?*

54

Discuss each of the persons in turn. Then, by family agreement, decide which of these needs you would best be able to answer. Choose a form of service which involves as many family members as possible. Be certain that the project is suited to your family circumstances. Choose something concrete and practical which can be completed in a short period of time.

These are some sample projects to assist your thinking:

—visit a shut-in
—invite a lonely person to your home
—bring a gift to someone who rarely receives one
—write a letter to someone far away
—get together with relatives you have not seen in a while
—prepare a gift of food or clothing for someone in need
—earn or save money for a worthy cause
—offer to run errands or do odd jobs for someone who is elderly or sick
—promise to say something kind and encouraging to at least one person each day

When the family has completed plans for its project and has carried them out, all may wish to gather again to discuss the results of their efforts and to plan further ways of helping others as a family.

Getting Ready for Mass

After the priest has read the Gospel and talked to us, we stand and pray. We ask God to remember our needs and help us. We pray for the poor and hungry. We pray for the sick and lonely. We pray for those who have died. We pray for our family and friends.

As each need is named, we pray together: **Lord, hear our prayer.** Perhaps some other words are used in your church. What are they?

As we pray we remember that God helps us through one another. We must be ready to help our family and friends when they need us. **Can you think of someone for whom you would like to ask God's help when you are at Mass?**
Write that person's name here.

LESSON 6
Jesus Invites Us to Bring Our Gifts to the Father

Brendan sat up in bed. The sky was beginning to change from gray to blue. He could already hear kitchen noises, and a very good smell was coming through the crack in the bedroom door.

Today was the day he had been waiting for. It was Thanksgiving morning. That meant turkey and pie and a visit from his cousins.

He jumped out of bed and put on his oldest clothes. He would save the good ones for later. For now there was lots of work to be done.

His sister, Val, and his brother, Tom, were already peeling vegetables when he arrived in the kitchen. As he ate his cereal he asked, "What's my job, mom?"

"Why don't you help your father bring extra chairs from the attic? Then you can help me polish the silverware."

Brendan liked to polish the silverware. It had belonged to his grandmother and they used it only on important days. It was fun to rub and rub until the shine came out.

Then they set the table. Val made sure that Brendan put the forks and spoons in the proper places. "Everything looks great, mom!" Brendan said enthusiastically as he ate one of the special holiday pickles.

"Everything but you!" his mother laughed.

So he ran to change his clothes. Tom helped him with his tie.

The house was ready. The table was ready. He was ready. But it still wasn't time for the company to come. Brendan was feeling too happy to sit still and look out the window. So he pulled out his crayons and drawing paper and colored a picture of a smiling turkey with the word, "Welcome!" underneath. The whole family liked it.

"Quick," his dad said, "Let's tack it on the front door before they get here."

As they stood admiring their work Brendan said to his father, "You know what, dad? I think this will be our best Thanksgiving ever."

And he was right.

How does your family celebrate Thanksgiving?
What preparations must be made?
Do you have a special job to do?
Why do you suppose Brendan and his family had such a happy day?

In the space below draw the picture of a table prepared for Thanksgiving dinner. Below the picture name some of the things for which you might want to thank God our Father on Thanksgiving Day — or today.

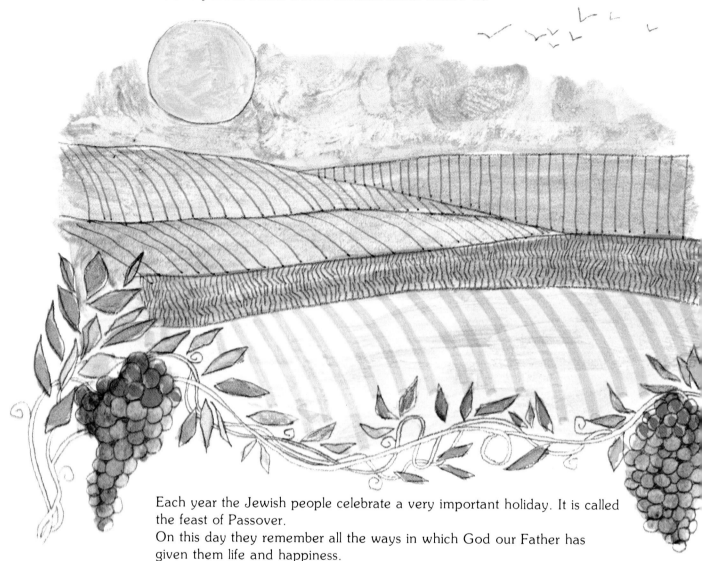

A Story from Mark 14:12-16 and Luke 22:17-19

Each year the Jewish people celebrate a very important holiday. It is called the feast of Passover.

On this day they remember all the ways in which God our Father has given them life and happiness.

They say "thank you."

They promise to love Him and to love one another.

They eat a special meal together as a sign of this love they share.

Jesus used to eat this Passover meal with His apostles.

Each year they looked forward to this day.

One year when Jesus and His apostles went to the big city of Jerusalem to celebrate the feast of Passover, they did not feel so happy as usual.

Jealous people there did not like Jesus.

They were following Him everywhere and causing trouble.

"Maybe Jesus will be too worried and too busy to get ready for the special meal," the apostles thought.

"We had better remind Him."

On the day when all the people were preparing their lambs for dinner (lamb was the special food eaten at this meal), the apostles went to Jesus and said, "Where do you want us to go and get Your Passover meal ready?"

They should have known that Jesus would not forget.
He had already chosen the house where they would share the feast.
He sent two of His friends to this place.
There they found a large upstairs room which had been fixed up and furnished according to Jesus' orders.
The two men worked hard preparing the lamb, the bread and wine, and the special vegetables for the meal.
They wanted it to be the best Passover feast which they and Jesus had ever shared.

When Jesus and the rest of His friends arrived, how pleased they must have been to see the room and the table all ready for the party.
Jesus knew that the work His friends had done was a sign of their love for Him and for each other.

Jesus sat in His place of honor.
The good foods on the table reminded Him of all the good things God our Father provides for His children.

He lifted a cup of wine from the table and said a "thank you" to God:

> *Blessed are You, O Lord our God,*
> *King of the universe,*
> *Who creates the fruit of the vine.*

Then He took some of the bread in His hands and said a prayer like this one:

> *Blessed are You, O Lord our God,*
> *King of the universe,*
> *Who brings forth bread from the earth.*

When Jesus passed the bread and wine for His friends to share, He knew this would be the best "thank you" of all.
When we share God's gifts joyfully together it is a way of giving ourselves to Him as one family.

Thinking About the Story

Do you know how bread is made?

The bread comes from the plant called "wheat" which God has given us.

We need a lot of wheat to make bread for everyone. So the farmer saves many of the small wheat grains or seeds. God has given each seed power to grow into a big stalk of wheat. The farmer helps the seed to grow.

The farmer plants these grains in the rich earth which is God's gift. The earth has the food which the grain needs. God's gifts of sun and rain also help the new wheat plant to grow.

When the wheat is ripe, men come on large machines to cut it down. They separate and sort the grains.

Other people grind the grains to make flour.

Bakers take this flour and mix it with other good things which are gifts from God.

They put it in the oven, and in a little while: It's bread!

Think of all the people who work with God's gift of wheat so that we may have bread to eat. When we use God's gifts to care for one another and give one another joy, it is like giving God a present. God gives His gifts to help us love Him and love one another as a happy family.

Do you know how people use God's gift of grapes to make wine? Perhaps someone at your house can help you find the answer.

Our Eucharist celebration is a meal like the Last Supper. We share bread and wine as a sign that we belong to Jesus and to one another.

The bread we use at Mass is not like the bread we eat at home. It is flat. Usually it is round and white. We call these small, round pieces of bread "**hosts.**" During Mass Jesus will make this bread the gift of Himself to us.

The wine we use at Mass is mixed with water. The wine and the water are poured from small pitchers, called cruets, into a large cup called a **chalice.** During Mass Jesus will make the wine the gift of Himself to us.

Do you know what the chalice at your church looks like?

A FAMILY CELEBRATION

Preparing for the Celebration

The family may gather together. Each member will write his or her name on a slip of paper. These slips will be folded and placed together in a dish. Each person will choose one of these slips, but will not tell whose name he or she has drawn.

Explain that each is to do an act of kindness for the person whose name he or she has received. If possible this act is to be done secretly. These acts of kindness are to be done before the special family meal is eaten.

The family may then plan a special table setting for this meal. An effort may be made to use God's gifts in making the table attractive. A flower arrangement, homemade candles, candlesticks, placemats, napkin rings, a centerpiece, a wall-hanging would all be ways for family members to give praise to God by using His natural gifts to create something which would bring joy to the entire family. Every person in the family should contribute to the table setting in some way.

Each person should also prepare a card for the one whose name he or she has chosen. The card should be of original design, but the sample on the Activity Sheet for this lesson may offer inspiration. The child preparing for First Communion may use the sample in making his or her own card. (see p. 119).

Read over the sample celebration which follows. Adapt it to your family style. Assign roles. Become familiar with prayer responses.

A Table-Setting Ceremony

On the day of the meal all things needed for setting the table may be set out in a convenient place. Family members may form a procession, each carrying some article to the dining table. The "procession" may need to make several trips before the setting is complete. It may be desirable for one family member to direct the actual setting of the table as the others bring the needed articles. As a final touch, the appropriate card may be put at each person's place. Playing of soft background music during the procession may help to give the setting of the table a more ceremonial and reverent tone.

The Offering of Thanks

When all are seated at the table, the head of the family may raise a small loaf of bread (preferably homemade) in his or her hands and say the following prayer:

Blessed are You, Lord, God of all creation.
Through Your goodness we have this bread to offer,
which earth has given and human hands have made.

All: *Blessed be God for ever.*

He or she may then raise a cup of wine (or grape beverage) and offer the following prayer:

Blessed are You, Lord, God of all creation.
Through Your goodness we have this wine to offer,

fruit of the vine and work of human hands.

All: *Blessed be God for ever.*

The head of the family may then offer the following invitation:

Let us read the cards at our places. Our kindnesses to one another are the best way we have of saying "thank you" to God our Father. He gives Himself to us in His gifts. We give ourselves to Him by using these gifts to bring happiness and help to one another.

Family members may read the cards and thank one another. The cards may then be placed in the center of the table, possibly between two candles, as a sign that these acts which draw the family together are a gift of thanks to God our Father. If desired, a symbolic loaf of bread and cup of wine may complete the centerpiece arrangement.

Getting Ready for Mass

During Mass you will see the priest raise the gold plate on which the large, round piece of bread called the **host** has been placed. He prays:

Blessed are You, Lord God of all creation. Through Your goodness we have this bread to offer, which earth has given and human hands have made.

We answer:
Blessed be God forever.

Then the priest lifts the large cup, called the chalice, in which the wine has been placed and says:

Blessed are You, Lord God of all creation. Through Your goodness we have this wine to offer, fruit of the vine and work of human hands.

We answer:
Blessed be God forever.

Can you learn this by heart and remember to say it at Mass?

Katie sat on the bench in the playroom, swinging her foot and counting the tiles on the floor. All the other children had gone home. Katie was wishing she could go home too, but her dad was late again.

At last she saw Mrs. Thompson walk to her office window and look through the blind. "He's here, Katie," she called cheerfully, and came over to help her put on her coat.

As Katie ran across the yard to the car, her dad opened the door. "Hop in, Pumpkin," he said. "I'm sorry I'm late. I had to finish some work before I could leave." He smiled down at her. "I bet it seemed like a long day, didn't it?"

Katie nodded and cuddled closer to him. Being near him always helped her lonesome feeling to go away.

"Guess what's for supper," he teased her.

"Burgers and fries," she guessed.

"Once a week is enough for that stuff," he said. "Tonight I'm making you a real dinner: steak and mashed potatoes, and vegetables and chocolate pudding for dessert."

"May I whip the cream?" Katie begged.

"Would I ever refuse some help?" her dad asked.

The supper tasted good, but the house always felt empty to Katie since her mother was gone. She guessed her dad felt it too. He talked more loudly than before and he made more jokes. When it grew dark he would turn on all the lights and play the radio.

After supper they did the dishes. As the last dish was put away her dad said, "Homework time!" Katie didn't mind. It was another chance to sit close to him.

While she was taking her bath her dad checked to be sure she had clean clothes for school the next day. He looked at his watch when she came downstairs all ready for bed. "I guess it's O.K. for you to watch T.V. a little while," he told her.

He fell asleep before the program ended and Katie had to tug his arm when it was time for him to kiss her goodnight. "Sleep well, Katie my girl," he said.

Each night in bed Katie would listen in the dark and try to guess what he was doing from the sounds she heard: packing their lunches, doing the wash, listening to a ball game.

Sometimes when she saw the tiredness in her dad's eyes, or felt his loneliness, it hurt her inside. So she would draw a special picture for him in school or clean her room without being told. Maybe he knew how she felt too, because at times like that he would squeeze her and say, "You know, Pumpkin, it may not be easy, but FOR YOU—it's worth it!"

Name some of the ways in which Katie's dad took care of her.

Why may it have been hard for him to do some of these things?
How did Katie thank her dad?
Who cares for you in these ways?

Try to remember a time when someone did something kind for you—
something that was not easy.
How can you say "thank you?" **Write your idea here.**

A Story from Luke 22:14-19 and Matthew 26:26-28

When Jesus sat with His friends to share their last supper together, He had
fear and sorrow in His heart.
He knew His jealous enemies would soon come to arrest Him.
They had been calling Him names and telling lies about Him.
They had said to the people, "Jesus is not really God's Son.
He is a selfish man who only wants to be a rich and powerful king.
He does not really love God. He does not really love you."

Jesus knew these men wanted to kill Him.
He could have run away. But He would not leave us.
Jesus did love God the Father with all His heart.
Jesus did love every one of God's children—even those who were cruel
and unkind to Him.
Very soon He would show His great love for His Father and for us in the
most difficult way of all—by dying on the cross.

Sharing bread and wine at the Passover meal had always been one way
the Jewish people showed their love for God and one another.
This would be the last time Jesus and His friends shared this meal
together.
Jesus wanted His friends always to remember this night.
He wanted them to remember that His love for us is so great that He was
willing to give His life, to shed His blood for us.

So Jesus said, "I have wanted so much to eat this Passover meal with you before I suffer!"

Then He took the bread in His hands and offered a prayer of thanks to God, just as He had done at every other Passover meal.

But as He broke it in pieces and handed it to His apostles, He said new words they had never heard before:

"Take and eat it. This is My body which is given for you."

The bread He invited them to eat together was not ordinary bread any longer.

It was His life which He was offering to them as a sign of His love.
He was giving them Himself.

At the end of the meal Jesus lifted a cup of wine to share with His friends and said, "This is My blood which I will shed for you."
When the apostles drank from the cup, it was no longer ordinary wine they were receiving.
They were drinking in the life of Jesus.
He gave them His life as a sign of His great love.

"Do this in memory of Me," Jesus told them.
Always when those who believe in Jesus gather to share the bread and wine as He has asked us to do, we repeat the words which He spoke at that Last Supper:
"This is My body given for you. . . .
This is My blood shed for you."

We remember how Jesus died on the cross so that we may belong to God and one another now and forever.
But we are not sad. We are joyful.
Jesus is alive and with us still.
Death could not take Jesus away from us. He is with us always in a new and wonderful way.
His Spirit living in us helps us to love one another as Jesus loves us.

A FAMILY CELEBRATION

When the family is gathered together, ask each person, during a certain number of days, to become more aware of the following:

—the ways in which every other member of the family shows his or her love. Occasions when this giving is not easy for the person should be especially noted.

—at least one time when he himself or she herself performed a loving action which was difficult for him or her.

Having done this, each may select or create a sign of his or her gift to the family (for example, the family "chauffeur" might choose car keys; the "cook" might choose a kitchen utensil; the one who cares for the family pet, a can of dog food). If preferred, a more general sign of one's desire to give to the family may be created (for example, a heart, a cross, a flower). The child preparing for First Communion may wish to use the idea provided on the Activity Sheet for this lesson found on p. 121. Insofar as possible family members should be encouraged to create original signs of their gifts to the family. Specific direction and suggestion should be minimal.

The sample celebration which follows may then be examined and adapted as necessary. Roles may be assigned.

A SAMPLE CELEBRATION

(Note: This celebration may appropriately be used at meal time.)

When all is prepared, a time may be chosen for the family to gather. A table should be placed in the center of the family circle. A crucifix or cross may be placed on the table as a remembrance of Jesus' gift of Himself for us.

The head of the family may invite each person in turn to share his or her "gift" with the family and to explain its meaning. This explanation should be simple and spontaneous (for example: I am giving a light bulb because I have tried hard to remember to turn off the lights when I leave a room. This is my gift of myself to you. Or: I am giving this bar of soap because I am trying to take my bath as soon as mom tells me, so she won't have to yell at me. This is a sign of my love for you.)

After explaining his or her gift, the person may hand it to the one next to him. The individual who receives the gift may then express thanks to the giver for this and for any other act of self-giving which he or she may have noticed (for example: Thanks. I especially want to thank you for taking my turn to do the dishes so that I could play football.)

This speaker will then hand the gift to the one next to him or her, and so on until all have had a chance to receive it and express their thanks to the giver.

The giver may then place the gift in the center of the table near the cross which represents the self-gift of Jesus.

When all have had an opportunity to share their gifts, the following prayer may be said.

Leader: *The Lord be with you.*

All: *And also with you.*

Leader: *Lift up your hearts.*

All: *We lift them up to the Lord.*

Leader: *Let us give thanks to the Lord our God.*

All: *It is right to give Him thanks and praise.*

Leader: (These or similar words may be used.)
   Thank You, Father, for giving us to one another, for making us a family.
   You have shown Your love and care for us in many ways (present and past signs of God's care for the family may be mentioned: strength to meet difficulties, healing of an illness, obtaining of suitable employment, answering of a financial need, etc.)
   We thank You for sending Jesus Your Son to live among us and to die for us as a sign of Your great love for all Your children.
   May the memory of His death and resurrection help us to be more generous in loving one another, even when it is difficult.

Getting Ready for Mass

The most important prayer of all during Mass is the "Eucharistic Prayer." This prayer tells the story of the Last Supper. Listen carefully. You will hear the words which Jesus spoke as He shared the bread and wine with His apostles:

Take this, all of you, and eat it: this is My body which will be given up for you.

Take this, all of you, and drink from it: this is the cup of My blood. . . . It will be shed for you and for all people so that sins may be forgiven. Do this in memory of Me.

The bread and wine on the altar are not ordinary food anymore. Jesus is present to share His life and love with us as He did with His apostles at the Last Supper.

We welcome Jesus.
We remember how He died for us.
We say: **Christ has died.**
We remember how He rose to new life, and is with us now.
We say: **Christ is risen.**
We remember that Jesus is waiting to welcome the whole world to heaven where we will share His happiness forever.
We say: **Christ will come again.**

Can you learn these "remembering" prayers by heart?

Reader: (The story of the Last Supper on pp. 69-71 of this lesson may be read aloud.)

Leader: (After a moment of silence family members may be encouraged to share any personal thoughts on the story and the celebration itself. When all who wish to do so have spoken, the following prayer may be introduced.)

As a sign of our gratitude to Jesus for dying on the cross and as a sign of our gratitude that He is with us now and forever, let us pray together:

All: *Christ has died. Christ is risen. Christ will come again.* (This may be sung, if desired.)

Bread may then be broken and shared. A cup of wine or grape beverage may also be passed. Family members may wish to offer words of thanksgiving, peace or love to each other as they pass the bread and the cup.

(Note: Following this celebration members of the family may wish to create a centerpiece for their table using the crucifix and the gifts they have offered.)

LESSON 8
We Offer Ourselves to the Father with Jesus

Kim was the only child in the family. Often she wished she had a brother or sister to play games with her on rainy days or to sit on the other side of the seesaw when she went to the park.

There were plenty of boys and girls at school, of course. At recess time she would stand near the wall and watch them throwing the ball, jumping rope, or playing hopscotch. It looked like so much fun.

But Kim had never played those games before. She felt ashamed. When one of the girls looked her way, she would turn her head and pretend she was seeing something very interesting on the other side of the schoolyard. If she looked back, they might ask her to play. And what would she do then? So she just stood by the wall each day, feeling lonely and afraid.

One day the teacher came over to her and asked, "Why don't you join in any of the games, Kim?"

Kim looked down at her shoes, wishing hard that the teacher would walk away. But he just stood there with a kind and worried look on his face. Kim's heart began to pound. She could hardly whisper the words, "I don't know how to play."

"Would you like to learn?" the teacher asked.

Kim looked up. "Maybe," she said slowly. "But the kids would laugh at me."

"I have an idea," the teacher told her. "Come and see me after school."

That afternoon Kim went running home with a jump rope in her book bag. "Mom, look what the teacher gave me," she shouted as she ran into the house.

"Why didn't you tell me you wanted to learn to jump rope?" her mother asked. "I used to be the champion when I was in school."

Kim watched her mother jump rope in her stocking feet on the kitchen floor. She looked so funny. When she missed, they both laughed.

"Let me try!" Kim begged.

They went out in the driveway. Kim turned and jumped, and missed. She missed again. And again. Her face grew red. She turned harder and she jumped faster. And she missed.

She threw the rope on the ground. "I can't do it," she said. "I'll never be able to do it. It looks so easy when the other girls do it!"

"It looks easy," her mother said, "because it is easy once you know how. Maybe after supper we can try some more."

The next day in school Kim was staring at the girls, trying to see how they moved their feet. One of them noticed and called to her, "Would you like to play?"

Kim started to shake her head "no" again, but another girl said, "Come on, Kim. I'm tired of turning. You can do that, can't you?"

"Why, yes," Kim thought. "I guess I can do that." So she walked over and took one end of the rope.

Even turning was not so easy as it looked. At first the rope jerked in her hand and the girl at the other end kept saying, "Faster, Kim!" Slower, Kim!" She felt her cheeks growing hot. Her fingers squeezed the rope tighter and tighter. How she wished recess would end!

Then she began to feel a rhythm in the swing. She and her partner were working together. It was fun to turn really fast and hear the girls scream and laugh. Kim watched their feet very closely. Sometimes one of them missed, but no one seemed to mind. When the bell rang, Kim was surprised. "Recess went by so fast!" she said to her partner as they ran back to the classroom together.

That night she practiced and practiced. She kept getting tangled in the rope, but she did not give up. Once she jumped six times in a row without missing—what a wonderful feeling!

The next day she couldn't wait for recess time to come.

Why do you think Kim wanted so much to learn how to jump rope and to join the other games the boys and girls played?

Which do you think was harder: standing by the wall being afraid, or learning to play with the others?

Have you ever felt like Kim? Are there some things which you are afraid to do? Does this make you feel left out at times? Perhaps you would like to tell about it.

Can you remember a time when you were finally brave enough to do something that was hard for you? Did you feel wonderful like Kim did? Did it help you to make new friends? Tell about it.

The boys and girls in these cartoon pictures are unhappy. In order to feel happy about themselves, they must do something which is hard for them. **Draw cartoon pictures in the empty panels to show how each person can find a happy ending.**

A Story from John 21:1-14

After Jesus died on the cross the apostles were so lonely and afraid that they did not even dare to go outside. Then Jesus came to them, alive and happy.
While He was with them, they felt alive and happy too.
They felt brave enough for anything.

But when they did not see Jesus for a little while, they would begin to worry and wonder: Has Jesus left us for good? Will we ever see Him again?

One evening when they were having these gloomy, restless feelings, Peter said to some of his apostle friends, "I'm going fishing."
(Peter earned his living as a fisherman.)
The others were looking for something to do, so they said, "We will come with you."

At first it was pleasant on the cool, quiet lake.
Everyone helped to lower the big net into the water.
Each time they hoped it would come up filled with fishes, but—no luck.
So they would row a little farther and try again.
Down would go the net, and up it would come—empty.

The apostles' arms and backs grew tired.
They began to feel cold and hungry.
But each time they saw that empty net, they just had to try one more time.
They worked and worked all night, but not a single fish swam into the net.

As the sun was rising, they saw a man standing on the beach.
"Haven't you caught anything?" he called.

"Not a thing," they answered.

"Throw your net out on the right side of the boat, and you will find some," he told them.

What a strange thing for him to say!

"How does he know?" the apostles must have asked one another.
But they had tried so many times already, that it couldn't hurt to try once more.

What a surprise! When they threw the net out, they were not strong enough to pull it back into the boat—That's how full of fish it was!

John looked again at the man standing on the beach.
Then he turned to Peter.
"It is the Lord!" he whispered excitedly.

Immediately Peter knew John was right.

He could not wait to see Jesus.
He just grabbed his coat and jumped right into the water!
The other apostles were happy too, but the boat was very close to shore.
They brought it safely up on the beach with the net full of fish dragging behind.

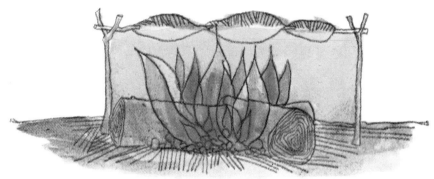

Jesus had built a fire.
On the fire was a fish.
Jesus had brought some bread as well.
The night had been very long and discouraging.
But the apostles quickly forgot their troubles.
They had never been happier than when they were eating breakfast on the beach with Jesus that morning.

Thinking About the Story

Jesus knows how we feel when we are afraid or worried about something. It was very hard for Him to die on the cross. But Jesus was brave. He remembered the great things His Father had done to help His people. Jesus knew He could trust His Father's love. He knew His Father would make everything turn out all right.

Now Jesus is happy with His Father forever. He loves His Father always. He loves us.

Even when Jesus' friends did not see Him or hear His voice, He was thinking of them and caring for them. He saw their troubles and was ready to help.

Jesus wants us to remember that He thinks of us too. He wants to help us belong to God our Father and to each other. He knows that sometimes this will not be easy for us. (Think of Kim and the boys and girls in the cartoon stories.)

Is there something you must do that is hard for you? You need courage. Perhaps you need someone to show you how. You need patience to try and try again.

Write a prayer in the space below asking the help of Jesus. He is always near.

A FAMILY CELEBRATION

Preparing for the Celebration

Gather the family together. Read over the sample celebration which follows. Adapt it to your family style. Assign roles. Become familiar with the prayer responses.

The following materials may be helpful:
- —a large candle to represent the Risen Jesus
- —a smaller candle for each family member
- —the "centerpiece" prepared for the family celebration of the previous lesson (see p. 73).

A SAMPLE CELEBRATION

(Note: This service may be held at meal time or any other time. An evening hour would add to the effectiveness of the candle-lighting ceremony.)

Reflecting on the Story

Reader: (The story of the great catch of fishes found on pp. 81-83 of this lesson may be read aloud.)

Leader: *Let us light the candle in the center of our circle. It will remind us that Jesus is with us, even though we cannot see Him. Jesus Who loved us enough to die for us is alive and happy now. He is thinking of us and caring for us, just as He cared for the needs of His apostles.*

Remembering Our Needs

Leader: *Now let us make a quiet place in our hearts.*
Think: Do I need the help of Jesus right now?
Is there something I should do which is hard for me?
Is there something of which I am afraid?
(Allow a few moments of silence. Then adapt the following suggestions to family circumstances.)

Do we need the help of Jesus in any of these ways?
Is there a job which we neglect or do carelessly because we dislike it (like cleaning our rooms, getting up on time, taking out the garbage, practicing the piano or doing homework)?
Is there a person whom we avoid or mistreat because it is not easy to be with him or her (for example, an elderly relative, a handicapped person, a person of another race or nationality, an unpopular child in school)?
Do we need courage because something is making us unhappy (like having a teacher or boss who is unkind, or being sick, or never having enough money, or wanting something we cannot have)?

The Lighting of the Candles

Speaker: *Jesus, we believe that Your Spirit lives in us. He gives us courage. He helps us to do what is hard for us. Dying on the cross was hard for You. But when Your Father raised You to new life on Easter Sunday it brought joy to You and to the whole world forever.*

We want to share Your new life. We want to grow in new ways. We want to love and help others. We want to give ourselves to the Father with You. Please be with us. Please help us.

Leader: *As a sign of our desire to give ourselves to God our Father along with Jesus, we will each take our small candle and light it from the Jesus candle.*

(The leader will invite each member of the family in turn to do this. Words are not required, but individuals may be encouraged to express their gift of themselves in a prayer which may be said aloud. These words may be general [Jesus I love You. I love Your Father. I give You my heart] or specific [as a sign that I give my heart to the Father with You, I will do my homework right after school each day this week]).

(When all have had their turns the following concluding prayer may be said.)
Jesus, please accept our efforts to love You (refer to centerpiece).
Help us to love You even more.

All: (Holding lighted candles)
Through Him, with Him, in Him, in the unity of the Holy Spirit,
all glory and honor is Yours, almighty Father,
forever and ever. Amen. Amen. Amen. (This may be sung if desired.)
(Candles may be blown out.)

LESSON 9
Jesus Makes Us One Family

Matthew's birthday was coming soon. "Let's make out your party list," his mother suggested. She was holding a paper with the names of all the boys and girls in Matt's class at school. She and Matt sat side by side and studied it together.

"Check Andy," Matt began, pointing to his friend's name. Then he stopped.

His mother looked over at him. "Who's next?" she asked.

"What about Andy's little brother?" Matt said. "He sure would love the cake and balloons. Do you think he would spoil the party?"

"I think it's worth the chance," his mother smiled and wrote in the name, "Peanut."

"May we write in Jack's name too?" Matt asked. Jack lived next door. He was older than Matt, but they played together often.

"Of course," his mother agreed, "but don't forget his sister, Cathy. She's in your class, isn't she?"

"But, mom," Matt objected, "if I invite her I'll have to invite all the girls."

"Girls like parties too," his mother laughed.

"Some of them are O.K., I guess," Matt admitted. His mother checked their names on the list.

"We should ask Phil," Matt remembered. "He always chooses me for his team." He looked over his mother's shoulder. "The list is getting pretty long, isn't it?"

"I have an idea," his mother said, sitting back in her chair. "Would you like to invite the whole class?"

"You mean even the kids who never invite me to their parties?"

"That's right," his mother told him.

Matt had to think a minute. "You know," he said at last, "that would be really great. No one would be mad at me. No one would feel left out!"

"It won't be a fancy party," his mother explained. "More children will mean less food for each."

"But you always plan such good games," Matt said eagerly. "We may have less food, but I bet we will have more fun."

Matt looked at the list once more. Then he looked·at his mother. "There's one kid that I want to ask," he said, "but I'm afraid."

"Why is that?" she asked.

"Pete acts like a baby sometimes. All the kids make fun of him."

"You're lucky, Matt," his mother said. "You make friends easily. Maybe if you are kind to Pete the others will stop teasing him so much."

So on Friday afternoon Matthew signed his name on every invitation, including one for Pete. He put them in the mail box himself. On Monday morning he could hardly wait to get to school.

"I'm coming to your party, Matt," Andy whispered as they were hanging up their coats.

"Is Peanut coming too?" Matt asked.

"Sure. Is he excited! He's never been to a birthday party before."

As Matt entered the classroom he noticed all the girls talking together. They looked over at him and giggled.

"Are you coming to my party, Cathy?" Matt called.

"We're all coming!" Cathy told him.

Matt put his hands in his pockets and began to grin. Everyone was smiling back at him. Then he noticed Pete. He was sitting at his desk pretending to read a book. No one was asking him about the party.

Matt walked over to him, "Are you coming to my party, Pete?" he asked.

Pete looked up in surprise. "Sure, Matt," he said shyly. "Thanks for asking me."

Matt couldn't think of anything else to say. He was about to turn away when Pete added, "I have a new puppy. I've already taught him some tricks. Would you like to see him?"

Now Matt was surprised. "O.K.," he said. "Maybe he'd like to come to the party too!"

When Matt turned around all the kids were looking at him and Pete. "Hey," he said. "I guess everyone is coming to my party—even Pete's puppy!"

Have you ever received an invitation to a party? How did it make you feel? Tell about it.

Do you think that day in Matt's class may have been a little different from other school days? Would the boys and girls have acted any differently toward each other? Try to imagine how it may have been. Tell about it.

Did you like the idea Matt's mother had of inviting all the boys and girls? Tell how you would feel if you went to a party with all the boys and girls in your class.

Not many children would be able to give a party as big as Matt's. But there are many other ways in which a person can show another boy or girl that he or she is willing to be a friend, such as sharing a toy or helping with homework. Can you think of two more ways of making a friend? DRAW ONE IN EACH OF THE SPACES BELOW.

Bread was a most important food in the land of Palestine where Jesus lived.

Each day people ate thick slices of fresh bread with their meals.
Bread gave them the energy to think and to work.
Bread made them healthy and strong.
Bread tasted good and filled them with content.

Jesus told the people, "I am the living bread."
He wanted them to understand:

"When you welcome Me into your heart and into your life as a Friend,
I will give you energy to love God our Father and one another;
I will give you strength and courage to do what is right;
I will fill you with peace and happiness;
My own goodness and love will begin to live and grow in you."

At the Last Supper Jesus took a piece of ordinary bread in His hands and made it a new kind of food.
He said to His friends, "Take and eat it. This is My body, which is given for you."

His friends reached out to receive this bread.
They ate it and made it a part of their own bodies.
They were not eating ordinary food.
They were really welcoming Jesus into their hearts, and into their lives.
They were asking Him to share with them His own Spirit of love.

90

Many grapes grow in the land of Palestine.
The picture on the opposite page shows what a grape vine looks like.
The stalk of the vine sinks roots deep into the earth.
The roots stretch out, soaking in water and foods which plants need to grow.
The food travels up the stalk, through the vine, to the branches.
As the branches drink in this food, they become thick and strong.
Dark green leaves and purple grapes grow from them.
They give food and joy to many people.

Jesus told His friends, "I am the vine, you are the branches. I chose you to go and bear much fruit." Jesus wanted them to understand:

"When you welcome Me into your heart
and let Me be your Friend,
I share My Spirit with you.
Just as the vine brings food and life to the branches,
My Holy Spirit living in you helps My great love to grow in your heart.
When you show this love in acts of kindness,
you are bearing good fruit."

Jesus took a cup of ordinary wine in His hands and made it a new kind of drink.
He said to His friends, "This is My blood shed for you."
When the apostles drank from this cup of wine, they were drinking in the Spirit of Jesus.
They were welcoming the gift of His great love.

91

Jesus wanted them to use this gift well.

He wanted them to share His love with each other, just as they were sharing the bread and wine.

So He told them, "This is the rule I want you to remember: I want you to love one another in the same way that I love you."

Then Jesus prayed to His Father and said, "Holy Father, keep My friends safe. I want them to be one just as You and I are one."

Each time we gather as a family at Mass we remember the new rule Jesus has given us.

We remember His prayer: I want them to be one.

When we reach out to take the bread and eat it, we welcome Jesus into our hearts.

We ask Him to feed us with His own Spirit of Love.

We ask Him to help us love one another so that we may be truly one family.

When our family sits around the supper table together, perhaps it may be a little noisy. Sometimes there are even quarrels and corrections. But we know that we belong to one another. We share the good and the bad because we love one another. When we eat the same meal from the same table, it is a sign of this belonging and love and willingness to forgive.

Jesus has given us a meal to share with the members of our Catholic family. We may not know all the people whom we see at Mass on Sunday, but we know that we belong to one another. The Spirit of Jesus lives in each of us. We share His life together. We are like branches on the same vine.

Receiving Jesus, the living Bread, into our hearts is our way of asking Jesus to help us grow in His love. Drying the dishes after supper or letting another person have the first turn or coming when we are called. Doing these things helps the love of Jesus to grow in our own hearts and in the hearts of others. It makes us truly one family as Jesus prayed we would be.

A FAMILY PRAYER CELEBRATION

Preparing for the Celebration

As a family, read over the sample celebration which follows. Adapt it to family circumstances. Assign roles. Examine the suggested activity as described on the Activity Sheet for Lesson 9 which is found on p. 123. The child preparing for First Communion may enjoy tracing and cutting a "branch" and one or two "bunches of grapes" for each member of the family. An older family member may be needed to assist in making the "vine." Notice what materials you may need for this activity, and choose a suitable working place.

A SAMPLE CELEBRATION

(Note: The first part of this celebration may be held in a work area where family members will have space to cut, paste, etc. The second part of the service may be held around the dining table. The entire service may be held at one time, or the two parts may be done on separate occasions.)

Preparing the Banner

Prepare the work area as suggested on the Activity Sheet for Lesson 9 found on p. 123.

Reader: (The story of the vine and branches found on pp. 90-92 of this
lesson may be read aloud.)

Leader: (The project may be explained in words similar to the following)
*We, as a family, have received the gift of Jesus' Spirit. When we try
to show kindness, forgiveness, patience, and generosity toward one
another, it is Jesus' own love in us that gives us the strength and
courage to act in this way. Together, let us make a poster of the
Jesus vine to remind ourselves that we are one because of the Spirit
of Jesus Who lives in us and helps us to bear good fruit each day.*

Prepare the poster or banner as directed on the Activity Sheet. If branches
have been prepared in advance, ask each person to print or write his or
her name on one branch using crayon or felt tip pen. These "branches"
may then be pasted on the vine using the model picture on the Activity
Sheet as a guide. Each person may then take one "bunch of grapes" and
draw or print on it one way in which he or she tries to "bear fruit" in the
family. (If desired, each person may prefer to prepare someone else's
bunch of grapes rather than his or her own. Acts of kindness noted in
previous prayer celebrations may be recalled and noted.) The bunches of
grapes may then be pasted on the appropriate branches. The entire banner
or poster may then be hung in the room where the family will eat together
(or used as a "runner" down the center of the table).

Gathered around the dining table, the following prayers may be said.

Leader: *Let us pray that we and all people everywhere may be one family, loving one another as Jesus loves us.*

All: (Joining hands, if desired) *Our Father. . . .*

Leader: *Deliver us, Lord, from every evil,*
and grant us peace in our day.
In your mercy keep us free from sin
and protect us from all anxiety
as we wait in joyful hope
for the coming of our Savior, Jesus Christ.

All: *For the kingdom, the power, and the glory are yours, now and forever.*

Leader: *Lord Jesus Christ,*
You said to Your apostles:
I leave you peace, My peace I give you.
Look not on our sins, but on the faith
of Your Church,
and grant us the peace and unity of Your Kingdom
where You live for ever and ever.

All: *Amen.*

Leader: *Let us offer each other the sign of peace.*

All: (Each person may offer every other a handshake or hug as a sign of peace, saying)
The peace of the Lord be with you always.

And also with you.

Leader: (Breaking bread in enough pieces for those present)

Lamb of God, You take away the sins of the world: have mercy on us.

All: *Lamb of God, You take away the sins of the world: have mercy on us.*
Lamb of God, you take away the sins of the world: grant us peace.

(Each person may then receive a piece of the bread from the leader. As he or she does so, she may wish to offer a prayer for the family in his or her own words.)

Leader: (After all have eaten the bread) *Jesus, we have shared this bread as a sign that we want to belong to You. We want Your Spirit to live in us. With the help of the Spirit we want to bring Your healing love to one another and to everyone we meet. We want to bear good fruit so that Your prayer at the Last Supper may become real. Help us to be one as You and the Father are one.*

All: *Amen.*

Getting Ready for Mass

You will walk to the altar slowly and quietly when it is time to receive Jesus in Holy Communion. You will stand before the priest or minister of the Eucharist. He or she will hold the round, flat, piece of bread, called the "host" for you to see. He or she will say:

The Body of Christ (This means, "It is Jesus.")

You will answer:
Amen. (This means, "I believe in Him.")

If you plan to receive the host on your tongue, tilt your head back slightly, open your mouth wide, and make a table with your tongue. (See picture.) You can also choose to have the host placed in your hand. After it has been placed there, move to one side, pick it up with your free hand, and place it in your mouth. You swallow the Bread. Chew, if this helps you to swallow it. Then you will think of Jesus Who has come to you. You will speak to Him in your heart.

What will you want to say to Jesus?

LESSON 10
Welcoming Jesus

Each Sunday the members of God's Catholic family come together to remember God's great love and to give thanks

Sometimes we call this "thank-you" celebration the Mass.
Its other name is "Eucharist."
Eucharist means "thanksgiving."

A celebration means coming together with our friends to show how happy we feel about something wonderful that has happened.

We show our joy and thanks by
     listening and talking to one another
     singing and dancing
     bringing gifts
     playing games
     sharing food

Draw a picture of one way in which you celebrate with your family and friends.

Jesus Himself celebrated the first Eucharist at the Last Supper.
On that night before He died Jesus and His friends celebrated their thankfulness to God our Father for His great goodness and love.

Jesus wanted all those who believe in Him to share His Eucharist celebration.
At that first Eucharist He told His apostles:
"Do this in memory of Me."
Jesus invites each of us to join with Him and all God's Catholic family in giving thanks to our Father.

These are the ways in which we join with Jesus in showing our love for God and each other at the Eucharist.

We gather together and sing our joy.

We greet God and each other:
In the name of the Father, and of the Son,
and of the Holy Spirit. Amen.
The Lord be with you.
And also with you.

**We ask forgiveness of God
and each other.**
Lord, have mercy.
Christ, have mercy.
Lord, have mercy.

**We ask the help of God our Father for
ourselves and all His needy children.**
Do you know someone who is in special
need of God's love and care?
Write your prayer for that person here.

**We listen as God speaks to us
through the Bible.**
When our priest reads to us from the Gospel,
we hear the words and deeds of Jesus.

We bring bread and wine to the altar.
Bread and wine are made from God's gifts of wheat and grapes. We use these gifts to make bread and wine which give people joy. Using God's gifts to bring joy to others is our way of saying "thank you" to Him.

We give thanks together for all the ways God has shown His love and care.
We do what Jesus did at the Last Supper.
Our priest speaks for Jesus.
He says the words Jesus said at the Last Supper:

> This is My body given for you . . .
> This is My blood shed for you . . .

The bread and wine are no longer ordinary.
They have become the gift of Jesus' life given to the Father for us.

We join with Jesus in offering our life and love to the Father.
As our priest raises the bread and wine we say:

> Through Him,
> with Him,
> in Him,
> in the unity of the Holy Spirit,
> all honor and glory is Yours,
> almighty Father,
> forever and ever.
> Amen. Amen. Amen.

We prepare to welcome Jesus into our hearts.
We ask forgiveness of one another.
We show that we are one family
   by praying the **Lord's Prayer** together:
   Our Father who art in heaven . . .
   by giving one another a sign of peace:
   The peace of the Lord be with you always.
   And also with you.

We go to the altar as one family.
We share the Bread of Life which is Jesus Himself.
How happy God's family will be on the day *you* join them in welcoming Jesus.
The priest will hold the Bread for you to see.
You will eat the Bread which the priest gives you.
You will be welcoming Jesus into your heart.
What will you say to Jesus?
Write your prayer here.

Now we are ready to go out to love and serve the Lord.
Our celebration is almost over.
We have welcomed Jesus into our hearts.
Our priest speaks for Jesus and blesses us:

May almighty God bless you,
the Father, and the Son,
and the Holy Spirit.
Amen.
Go in peace to love and serve the Lord and one another.

We sing a glad song together.

A FAMILY CELEBRATION
for the Eve of First Communion

Preparing for the Celebration

During the week before First Communion Day gather the family together. Suggest that on the evening before the Mass of First Communion all family members join with the child in preparing their minds and hearts for this great occasion.

Read over the sample celebration which follows. Adapt it to family circumstances. Assign roles. If desired, the role of leader may be divided among several family members to give more persons an active part.

Note that the making of a special cake or bread is suggested. Perhaps the First Communion child could assist in preparing and decorating it.

SAMPLE CELEBRATION

(Note: This celebration may appropriately be held on the evening before the Mass of First Communion, during a quiet time shortly before the child is to retire for the night.)

Greeting One Another

Leader: *Let us join hands as one family. Remember that Jesus is present with us. Let us join with Him in offering love and thanks to God our Father. Tonight we are especially thankful to God for ____(name of child)____ . We are grateful that (he/she) will be able to join us in welcoming Jesus in Holy Communion. Let us show our thanks and joy.*

All: (A song may be sung, perhaps one which has been learned for the Mass of First Communion. If this is not possible, all may clap for joy.)

Leader: *We will make the* **Sign of the Cross** *together as a sign of the faith we share.*

All: *In the name of the Father, and of the Son, and of the Holy Spirit. Amen.*

Leader: *The Lord be with you.*

All: *And also with you.*

Asking Forgiveness of One Another

Leader: *As we prepare to thank God with Jesus, our minds and hearts should be free of mean or unforgiving thoughts. Think back over this day, this week. Have you or I done anything to hurt someone else? to bring unhappiness to the family or to others? Let us be very still and think of this carefully.*
(Allow a time of silence.)
Now let us ask God's forgiveness together.

(Note: The family may choose to prepare its own prayers or to offer spontaneous prayers asking forgiveness. The following prayers of contrition are merely examples.)

First Reader: *I am sorry for the times I have made someone feel unwanted or left out. Lord, have mercy.*

All: *Lord, have mercy.*

Second Reader: *I am sorry for the times I have hurt the feelings of others with teasing or unkind words. Christ, have mercy.*

All: *Christ, have mercy.*

Third Reader: *I am sorry for the times I made extra work for others by not doing my share. Lord, have mercy.*

All: *Lord, have mercy.*

Listening to God's Word

Leader: *Lord, we are truly sorry for the ways in which we have hurt others, forgetting Your love. Help us to remember now as we listen to the Good News of the Gospel. Help us to learn from Jesus, Your Son.*

Reader: *Alleluia.*

All: *Alleluia.*

Reader: *A story from the holy Gospel according to Luke. 24:13-35*
(All may make the **Sign of the Cross** on their foreheads, lips and hearts.)

All: *Glory to You, Lord.*

Reader: It was the first Easter Sunday, the day Jesus rose to new life.
Late in the afternoon two of Jesus' friends decided to take a walk to a nearby town.
On the way they talked to one another about what had happened to Jesus.
They felt very sad as they remembered how Jesus had died on the cross.
They had seen the tomb in the side of the hill where His dead body had been placed.
A big stone had been rolled in front of the door.
Strong soldiers guarded it.
On this Sunday morning, however, some of the women had come running to tell them that Jesus' tomb was empty.

He was not there! He was alive! He was happy!
But how could that be, these men wondered.
They had not seen Jesus. They were still feeling worried and sad.
Without Jesus to help them, what could they do?
As they talked, a stranger caught up with them and asked, "What are
you talking about as you walk along?"

They stood still with sad faces.

"Are you the only one who does not know what has happened?" they asked him.

They told the stranger about Jesus.

"We are sad," they said, "because Jesus is no longer with us to help us love God and one another."

Then the stranger said, "You are very foolish to feel sad. Haven't you read the Bible?"

Jesus was sent by God our Father.

The Father loves Him.

He has saved Jesus from death.

Jesus will live and bring life and joy to people everywhere forever and ever."

The stranger seemed so sure, that Jesus' friends began to feel better.

Maybe it was true. Maybe they would see Jesus again.

Perhaps all people could hope to be one family as Jesus had prayed they would be.

As they talked, they came near the village where the two men planned to spend the night.

"Stay with us," they begged the stranger.

"The day is almost over and it is getting dark."

So the stranger went in to stay with them.

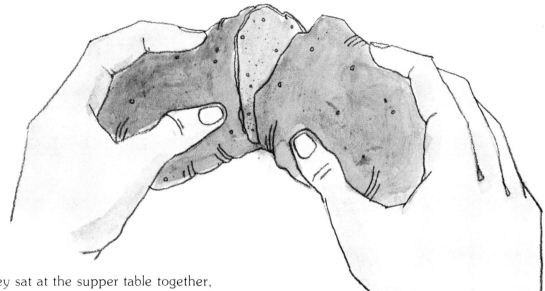

As they sat at the supper table together,
He took the bread in His hands and gave thanks to His Father.
Then He broke the bread in pieces and shared it with them.
As they took the bread, the two men remembered that Last Supper
with Jesus. A great joy began to sing inside them.
Ths One Who had shared their journey,
The One Who had spoken wise and comforting words, was not really
a stranger at all. It was Jesus!
Just as they turned to touch His hand, to call out to Him, He was
gone.
But the love He had shared with them was still burning like a fire in
their hearts.
Even though it was late, they could not wait to tell the apostles the
good news.
They ran all the way back to the city.
What a happy reunion they had that night!
This is the Gospel of the Lord.

All: *Praise to You, Lord Jesus Christ.*

Leader: *This story can remind us of our Eucharist celebration.*

(Give family members an opportunity to draw parallels which occur to
them.)

*Each day is something like a journey which we are taking. We start
out together. But we will be sad and unsure unless we remember that
Jesus is with us. At our Eucharist we are helped to remember the
presence of Jesus. He speaks to us, as He spoke to those men,
through the Bible. He helps us to understand that He is alive and with
us always. He helps us to know what we must do to grow in love for
the Father and for one another. Then He breaks bread with us as He
did at the Last Supper. He shares Himself with us in Holy Communion. Even though we cannot see Him, His Holy Spirit lives in us and
helps us to love one another as Jesus loves us. Like those two men,
we should want to go out from our Eucharist and tell everyone we
meet the Good News.*

Praying for Others

Leader: *One way in which we can share the good news is by noticing the needs of others and allowing Jesus to help them through us. Let us pray now for those who are in need of Jesus' healing love.*

All: (Those family members who wish to do so may mention needs of others, both those personally known to the family and those learned of through newspapers or T.V. As each petition is offered, all may answer: Lord, hear our prayer.)

Offering Ourselves to the Father with Jesus

(Note: A special cake or bread may be brought into the room and placed before the leader.)

Leader: *Blessed are You, O Lord our God, King of the universe, Who brings forth bread from the earth. Let us remember the many gifts of God to us. Let us think in our hearts what we can do to return that love. Perhaps we each would like to make a personal promise to God.* (Allow a time of silence.)
Perhaps there is one promise we can make as a family. (The family may wish to decide upon this promise at the preparation meeting and pray it aloud at this time. The promise could appropriately involve some form of service to others.)

Offering Thanks to the Father with Jesus

Leader: *The Lord be with you.*
All: *And also with you.*
Leader: *Lift up your hearts.*
All: *We lift them up to the Lord.*
Leader: *Let us give thanks to the Lord our God.*
All: *It is right to give Him thanks and praise.*
Leader: *Thank You, Father, for giving us to one another, for making us one family.*
   You have shown Your love and care for us in many ways. (Family members may be invited to offer thanks to God for specific blessings.)
   We are especially thankful to You that _____**(name of child)**_____
   _____ *will receive the gift of Jesus' life and love in Holy Communion tomorrow.*
   We thank You for sending Jesus Your Son to live among us and to die for us as a sign of Your great love for all Your children.
   May the memory of His death and resurrection help us to be more generous in loving one another, even when it is difficult.

Preparing to Share the Food

Leader: *Lord, as we share this food together we are remembering Your Last Supper. We want this happy meal to be a sign of our belonging to You and to each other. We are willing to share what we have in order to please You and bring joy to others. Be with us.*
   Let us pray together the prayer which Jesus taught us as a sign of our love for each other.
All: (joining hands) *Our Father. . . .*
Leader: *Let us offer each other a sign of peace and love.*

All: (Each family member may greet every other with a spontaneous gesture and word of peace. If preferred, the traditional greeting may be used:

> *The peace of the Lord be with you always.*
> *And also with you.*

The greetings offered to the First Communion child should reflect the family's good wishes for him or her.)

Sharing the Food

Leader: (As he or she breaks and distributes the bread or other food.)
Lord, help us to be one even as You and Your Father are one. Help us to love one another in the same way that You love us.

(Note: The food may be shared informally, in a party atmosphere.)

The Blessing

(Note: This action may take place whenever the family is ready to disperse, perhaps when it is time for the First Communion child to prepare for bed.)

Leader: *May almighty God bless us, Father, Son and Holy Spirit. Let us go in peace to love and serve the Lord.*
All: (Having made the **Sign of the Cross** with the leader.)
Thanks be to God.
(Each person may wish to offer a special blessing or gesture of affection to the First Communion child.
A song may be sung, or all may clap for joy.)

LESSON 1 ACTIVITY SHEET

Let Jesus know that He is welcome in your heart and in your home. Make a "Welcome, Jesus!" button for each member of your family. Cut out the large circle below. Use it as a pattern to trace a button for each person in your family. Decorate the button with words, colors and designs which show how happy you are that Jesus is with us always. The small samples on this page may help you to plan designs of your own.

Use the notes on this page to write "thank you" to each person in your family for something he or she has done to help you. Make more notes if you need them—you don't want to leave anyone out. Cut out the notes. Decorate them. Save them for the celebration described on pp. 21—22 of Lesson 2.

Perhaps others in your family would like to write "thank you" notes to you and to one another also. Why not ask them?

LESSON 3 ACTIVITY SHEET

Here is the outline of a lamb like the one which the shepherd lost. Cut it out. Use it to trace a lamb for each person in your family. Cut the lambs out and decorate them. Write the name of each person on his or her lamb. Save them for the celebration described on pp. 30—32 of this book. (If you like, soft balls of cotton may be pasted on each lamb to look like wool.)

LESSON 6 ACTIVITY SHEET

Here is a design you may use to make a card. The card will tell of a kind act you have done for the person who receives it. If you wish, you may give the card as part of the family prayer celebration for Lesson 6.

Prepare the card following the directions below. Decorate the front and back. On the inside write a message like this one:

Dear _____:

       I am the one who _____

_____

I love you.

        (Sign your name.)

Cut along solid lines. Then fold along dotted line.   119

LESSON 7   ACTIVITY SHEET

A cross stands for Jesus' gift of His life to us.

Jesus died on the cross as a sign of His great love for us.

You may use this cross as a sign of your love for your family.

Cut it out. Draw pictures or write words on it which show ways in which you help and bring happiness at home.

Your love for your family will then be joined to Jesus' love for them in one beautiful sign.

Bring the cross as your gift to the family prayer celebration for this lesson.